101 WAYS TO TEACH CHILDREN SOCIAL SKILLS

A READY-TO-USE, REPRODUCIBLE ACTIVITY BOOK

by Lawrence E. Shapiro, Ph.D.

ISBN10: 1-56688-725-9

ISBN 13: 978-1-56688-725-0

THE BUREAU® FOR AT-RISK YOUTH
Promoting Growth Through Knowledge
A Brand of The Guidance Group
1-800-99-YOUTH
www.guidance-group.com

TABLE OF CONTENTS

Note: A reproducible worksheet follows each activity marked with an asterisk.

BEING PART OF A GROUP

EXPRESSING YOUR FEELINGS

CARING ABOUT YOURSELF AND OTHERS

PROBLEM SOLVING

LISTENING: A TWO-WAY STREET

STANDING UP FOR YOURSELF

MANAGING CONFLICT

Introduction

Some children seem to be socially adept from birth, while others struggle with various challenges of social acceptance. Some children make friends easily; others are loners. Some children have self-control, and others have quick tempers. Some are natural leaders, while others are withdrawn.

Many aspects of social development seem to be an innate part of a child's temperament, but we also know that the environment can play an important part in shaping a child's social development. In the last ten years, psychologists have become increasingly aware that social skills can, and should, be taught. Many studies have shown that shy children can become more outgoing, aggressive children can learn self-control, and children who tend to be social isolates can be taught how to make friends.

There is no question that children with better social skills have a significant advantage in life. They not only experience the rewards of positive relationships, but they do better in school, have a better self-image, and in general, are much more resilient as they face life's inevitable challenges.

This book is designed to teach social skills to many different types of children, particularly those with social problems. Often labeled as having a social skills deficit, these children may be considered aggressive, socially isolated, or shy. The underlying concept is that to proceed through the expected stages of their social development, children should posses all the skills addressed by this book. Written for use by groups of children, such as a classroom or a counseling group, the activities are intended to help children in every aspect of their social development, as they relate their peers, their parents and their teachers. While many activities can be used with just one child, it is hard to argue with the concept that social skills are best learned in a social environment.

How To Use This Book

This book is divided into nine sections that comprise the major categories of social development. It can be used as the basis of a social skills curriculum, or as part of an educational or treatment plan to address specific social skills problems.

Approximately half of the activities, identified by an asterisk in the Table of Contents, include reproducible worksheets. These worksheets can be photocopied directly from the book, or they can be printed from the accompanying CD. The worksheets on the CD are in PDF format, and you will need Adobe Acrobat Reader to view and print them. This program can be downloaded without charge from www.Adobe.com.

Communicating

Effective communication, the foundation of social success, consists of many distinct skills. The activities in this section will help children communicate who they are to others and learn the skills that are so important in forming friendships.

Social communication is a "language" and children are born with differences in their ability to learn this language, just as they have other learning differences. But there is no question that, with practice and encouragement, effective communication can be taught.

This section begins by helping children understand and express what makes them unique. As children learn to convey their interests, their values, and even their problems, they increase their self-acceptance and self-confidence.

The next step is to help children learn the skills involved in making an initial connection with other children. Children need to know how to introduce themselves, how to develop a personal dialog with one child, and then how to maintain a conversation in a group. Many children who have problems in social skills choose the wrong tactics for interacting with other children. They may brag and try to get the attention of others, an approach that can often lead to group rejection. Other children may hang back, just observing the group, which may result in them being ignored.

It is not helpful to criticize children for their inappropriate behavior. Criticism may lead to self-consciousness, and even resentment. A better approach is to teach children new skills and let them experience the immediate rewards of new social success. The skills that children learn in this section will help them with adults, as well as with other children. And the more that parents and teachers model and encourage good communication skills in children, the more quickly these skills will be learned.

Learning Objective: To learn more about each group member; to recognize that although people have different interests, they are alike in many ways

Skill: Social communication, social awareness

Ask the children to look around at the other group members, noticing ways they are different and ways they are alike.

Tell them:

> Most groups have something in common. For example, in this class you are all approximately the same age, and you are all learning the same things as the other children in your grade. Members of a sports team share an interest in their sport. In a computer club, the members are all interested in computers. At the same time, the individual members of these groups have their own interests and traits. Each one of us is totally unique, even though we have things in common with the other people in the group.

Distribute paper and writing materials. Ask the children to write a few sentences focusing on something they think is either special or unique about themselves—perhaps a talent, a favorite hobby, or a special experience they have had. At the bottom of their paper, have them write two or three of their physical traits (e.g., long hair, brown eyes) to make it easier for the others to guess whose paper is being read.

Put the papers into a basket or shoebox, and have children take turns choosing a paper to read aloud. As each paper is read, the others try to guess whose it is. When someone guesses correctly, the "special person" talks more about what he has written. The other children are given an opportunity to add to the conversation, relating their own experiences or interests to whatever the "special person" has focused on.

The person who guessed correctly is the next to choose a paper, and the activity continues until all the papers have been shared.

Learning Objective: To allow members of the group to get to know each individual's unique preferences and experiences

Skill: Self-awareness, awareness of differences

Tell the group:

> *All people have preferences and interests that are unique to them. Through exploring everyone's favorite things, some people will find that they have similar interests. Being aware of these similarities can help people talk to each other and can even lead to friendship.*

On a blackboard or large sheet of paper, list the following:

Activities	School subjects	Places
Sports	Foods	Colors
Hobbies	Music	Fun things to do

Leave enough room between each category to write in individual interests and names, e.g:

Sports
  Basketball–Kate

Hobbies
  Coin Collecting–Corey

Each child takes a turn telling one favorite thing in each category. If time is an issue, ask children to choose just three or four categories. Under each heading, write the child's name and interest. Some children will ultimately have the same favorite things and should be listed together (e.g., Basketball – Kate, Sal, Peter, and so on).

If time allows, small groups of children who have similar interests should be given a five-minute opportunity to share their experiences.

Learning Objective: To recognize personal values and why they are important to an individual; to allow other members of the group to get to know each other

Skill: Self-awareness, awareness of differences

Ask the children to define "values." Listen to their answers and write them on the blackboard or a large sheet of paper.

When everyone has had a turn, tell the group:

> *A value is a personal belief or feeling that something is important and worthwhile. It can be something you love to do, a way you choose to live your life, or even an idea. People have their own values; there are no right or wrong ones. Without your even thinking about it, values guide the way you behave and your decisions in life.*

Using Activity Sheet 3, give examples of different values. Ask the children to think about their personal values, and then distribute the activity sheet.

After they have completed the activity sheet, have several children choose one of their most important values and discuss why they feel it is important.

My Values

Name ———————————————— Date ————————————

From this list, circle three values that are very important to you. You may add your own on the lines at the bottom of the list, but still choose three.

Having good grades

Having fun

Spending time with my family

Having good friends

Honesty

Being a good athlete

Being creative

Being famous

Freedom

Helping others

Being rich

Being popular

_____   _____

Which value is most important to you? _____

_____

Why is this value so important to you? _____

_____

What value do you think your parents would choose as most important?

_____

What value do you think your closest friend would choose as most important?

_____

Introducing Yourself

Learning Objective: To teach children the proper way to introduce themselves

Skill: Making friends

Tell the group:

There are specific steps that people usually follow when they introduce themselves to others. When people are meeting for the first time, it's polite to tell each other their names. They try to appear friendly and interested in the person they are meeting. Grownups usually shake hands too. First impressions make a difference, so when you meet someone new:

- *Stand up*
- *Look the other person in the eye*
- *Smile*
- *Say, "Hi. I'm_____."*

Choose two children to role-play introducing each other. Then ask each child to choose another person and introduce one to the other, until the entire group has been introduced.

Learning Objective: To teach children the names of others in the group

Skill: Making friends

Explain to the group:

The first step in getting to know one another is to learn everyone's name. When you call people by their names, it shows that you are interested in them.

Children sit in a circle so that everyone's face can be seen. Choose a child to say his first name. The person sitting next to him then says her name, and so on, until the end of the circle is reached. The child who started then says the name of the person on his right, and so on around the circle.

Make a copy of Activity Sheet 5. Give it to the first student and have him write his name either horizontally or vertically. Pass the sheet around the circle until everyone's name is on the sheet.

When the activity is completed, have one student read the names. As each person's name is read, that person will raise her hand and say, "I'm

_____. "

The first person writes his name on the grid. The next person writes her name so that it crosses the first person's name. If there is no place to write your name so that it will cross another name, start a new section of the grid. At the end of the activity, everyone's name will appear on the page. If more room is needed, use another copy of this sheet.

Learning Objective: To allow group members to recognize the basis for relationships and get to know each other

Skill: Making friends

Tell the group:

> It's important to be able to get along with many different kinds of people. One of the first steps in the process is getting to know one person at a time. Each bit of information you learn about someone will help you build a relationship with that person.

Children sit in a circle with the facilitator. The facilitator turns to the person on her right, shakes that person's hand, and tells something about herself, either personal or impersonal. For example, she might say, "My name is Ms. Brady. I live in a green house." One child (or the facilitator) is designated as note-taker. On a piece of paper, she writes only the information the person has shared, not the person's name.

The person the facilitator greeted shakes hands with the person on his right, says his name, and again shares something about himself, e.g., "My name is Sandy, and I love chocolate." In turn, each person does the same.

When the end of the circle is reached, children take turns choosing people at random and repeating their names and what they revealed about themselves. For example, Mariel makes eye contact with Sandy and says, "Your name is Sandy and you love chocolate." Sandy then focuses on a person who has not been chosen, and he tells what that person revealed about herself.

The note-taker posts the notes on a wall or bulletin board. The next day, children are given the opportunity to identify whose information each note reveals. For example, one child will read the note that says, "I love chocolate," and say, "That's Sandy. He loves chocolate, and so do I!"

Learning Objective: To learn as much as possible about one person at a time

Skill: Making friends

Explain to the group:

> *It takes time to get to know people, and a good way to get to know others is to focus on one person at a time. Even though you think you may know something about a person from the way he dresses, talks, or acts, these things may not tell much about the real person at all.*

Distribute Activity Sheet 7. Divide the group into pairs and have each person write what they think they know about the other person. When everyone has finished their sheets, have the partners trade sheets.

One partner then tells the other what is correct and what is incorrect about what was written. He shares as much as possible—or as much as he wants—about himself with the other person.

The other partner then does the same.

Name _____ **Date** _____

On the lines below, write whatever you think you know about your partner.

Learning Objective: To help children recognize similar likes and dislikes

Skill: Making friends

Explain:

The phrase "having something in common" means that two people enjoy doing the same thing, or own something similar, or have a similar ability, and so on.

Distribute Activity Sheet 8 and ask the children to circle their interests. When they are done, have children choose partners, or divide the group into partners. Partners look at their sheets together, finding similar interests and talking to each other about them. Finally, partners share their different interests and tell each other about them.

Name _____ **Date** _____

I like to play...	My favorite thing to do is...	I live with my...
Basketball	Hang out with friends	Sister
Soccer	Read	Brother
Tennis	Play video games	Stepparent
Hockey	Write	Parent
Baseball	Listen to music	Grandparent
Other _____	Other _____	Other _____

I love to eat...	My favorite subject is...	When I grow up I want to be...
Italian food	History	A teacher
Chinese food	English	A firefighter
Southern food	Math	A doctor
Indian food	Science	A businessperson
Japanese food	Art	A pro sports player
Other _____	Other _____	Other _____

Learning Objective: To understand the importance of appreciating something about another person; to make another person feel good about himself

Skill: Making friends

Say:

> *When you give someone a compliment, you are saying something nice that makes him feel good. You can compliment something about the way he looks, something he has done well, something nice he's done for someone, something he owns, or something about one of his qualities, for example, that he's nice, strong, funny, etc.*

Then divide the group into groups of four. One person should:

- Look at any of the other three people, and use his or her name.

- Choose something that is appropriate to compliment.

- Using a sincere tone of voice, give the compliment (e.g., "I really like your shoes" or "You gave a great answer to the teacher's question.")

The person who has been complimented should say, "Thank you," and the person giving the compliment should respond, "You're welcome."

The person who has been complimented then chooses another person to compliment. Continue the activity until everyone has given and received a compliment.

When this activity is completed, ask the children to talk about the best compliment that they ever received. Why did they choose that compliment?

Accepting A Compliment

Learning Objective: To develop the ability to accept praise

Skill: Making friends

Ask the group for a definition of "compliment."

Tell them:

> *Being complimented encourages you to "keep up the good work." It usually makes you feel good about yourself, but sometimes it can be hard to accept a compliment. You might be embarrassed by what the person has said, or you might even feel that it isn't true. Perhaps, you don't like it when an adult compliments you in front of other children. You might think the other children will resent you for getting praise and feel that you are stuck-up.*
>
> *It is important to learn how to accept a compliment, just as it is important to learn how to give one. Complimenting is an important part of making and keeping friends.*
>
> *The simplest way to accept a compliment is just to say "Thank you." You can also give a compliment back. For example, if someone says, "I really like your new sneakers," you could say, "Thanks. I like yours too."*

Divide the children into pairs. Ask one person in each pair to go first and compliment his partner. The partner should say "Thank you" and give a compliment in return. The pair should repeat these steps three times.

Twice more, regroup the pairs and repeat the above directions. Make sure that each child has at least one chance to be the one who receives compliments (rather than initiates them).

Nonverbal Communication

Researchers in social communication note that nonverbal skills are actually much more important in communicating one's emotions than verbal skills. People pay attention not just to the words that are said, but also to the way they are said.

Some children are very skilled at nonverbal communication. They intuitively know how to convey their feelings by their nonverbal communication and how to "read" the feelings of others. Other children are very poor at nonverbal communication. Some psychologists think that up to 10% of children may have a nonverbal learning disability, which may be associated with serious social, emotional, and behavioral problems. With severe deficits in both the expressive and receptive components of nonverbal language, these children may seem inappropriate or strange, even to a casual observer. Such children will benefit from more intensive training in nonverbal communication and other social skills.

Nonverbal skills are divided into two main areas: body language and para-language. Body language consists of gestures, eye contact, posture, facial expression, an awareness of physical distance (referred to as proxemics), and even physical appearance. Paralanguage consists of everything about the way children communicate orally, except for their actual words. It includes voice tone, voice volume, voice inflection, accent, and any unusual articulation differences. Each element of a child's nonverbal behavior sends a visual message to other children, as well as to adults.

Like spoken communication, nonverbal communication is a two-way street. To improve their social success, children must learn to be aware of the nonverbal messages they send others and to read the emotional meaning behind the messages they receive.

As you go through the activities in this section, you may find that some children need more practice in certain areas than others. Make sure that children get the help that they need. As children learn better nonverbal skills, many aspects of their social and emotional development can improve.

Learning Objective: To help children recognize that how things are said can be just as important as what is said

Skill: Emotional communication, self-awareness

Ask the group what they think "tone of voice" means. Brainstorm definitions and write them on the blackboard or a large sheet of paper. Give examples of different tones of voice.

Explain that:

> *The tone of your voice—how you are actually saying something— communicates what you feel. Often, your tone of voice can give a stronger message than your words. Sometimes, how you say something can change the meaning of what you are saying. It can even give the message that you don't really mean what you are saying.*

Have the children sit in a circle. Going around the circle, ask them to give examples of voice tone that can change the meaning of what's being said or communicate the wrong feeling.

Example 1: The first child in the circle says, "I love ice cream" in a bored voice. The next child then says, "I love ice cream" as though she really does love it.

Example 2: The next child says, "I have so much homework!" in a happy voice. The next child says the same sentence in a tone he thinks appropriate, such as unhappy or angry.

Example 3: The next child says, "I think your shoes are cool" in a surprised voice. The next child says the same sentence in a tone she thinks appropriate, such as complimentary or friendly.

This activity can continue around the circle, with children making up their own statements. Follow up with a discussion of how voice tone affects the meaning of what's being said.

Voice Volume*

Learning Objective: To teach children the importance of using appropriate voice volume

Skill: Emotional communication, self-control

Ask the group why it's important to use the appropriate volume, or loudness, of voice in different situations. Brainstorm ideas and write them on the blackboard or a large sheet of paper.

Tell them:

> *Controlling your voice volume is a very important skill for getting along with other people. It means making your voice softer or louder, depending on the situation you are in. There are three basic voice volumes—soft, normal, and loud—and each is appropriate for different situations. When you use the best voice for a situation, you are also using self-control.*
>
> *Using the wrong voice volume—like talking loudly in a quiet place, or so softly that no one can hear you—can make other people feel uncomfortable, and it can make you feel as though you don't fit in. That's why you should first think about the situation you are in. Then, think about different voice volumes and choose the one that is most appropriate.*

Distribute Activity Sheet 12. After the children fill it out, ask them to think of other situations in which different voice volumes are appropriate. Then, have them discuss the reasons behind their answers.

Name _____ Date _____

Put a check under the voice volume that is appropriate for each situation.

	Soft	Normal	Loud
Studying at the library	☐	☐	☐
Cheering at a basketball game	☐	☐	☐
Shopping in a store	☐	☐	☐
Playing outdoors	☐	☐	☐
Playing indoors	☐	☐	☐
When someone is taking a nap	☐	☐	☐
When someone is on the phone	☐	☐	☐
When you are on the phone	☐	☐	☐
On the school bus	☐	☐	☐
Talking in the lunchroom	☐	☐	☐
Watching a movie	☐	☐	☐

Choose two of the situations above and tell why you would use a soft, normal, or loud voice.

_____

_____

Learning Objective: To teach children the appropriate use of eye contact

Skill: Emotional communication, self-awareness

Ask the group what they think "eye contact" means.

Tell them:

People speak with their eyes as well as their words. When people make eye contact, they look at the person to whom they are talking or listening. Making eye contact doesn't mean staring into the other person's eyes the whole time. It means looking at her every so often, so that she realizes you understand and care about what she is saying.

Without even speaking to you, other people are constantly giving you feedback about what you are doing. If you don't make eye contact with them, you won't be aware of their reactions. Likewise, if they don't look at you while they are speaking or listening to you, they can't fully know how you are feeling.

Distribute Activity Sheet 13. After one child has been the speaker and one the listener for all three situations, have them switch roles. Then, ask them to share their feelings about the three types of eye contact. Have a class discussion about what has been learned.

Name ——————————————————————— Date ———————————————

Tell your partner everything you did from the moment you got up this morning until now. While you are talking, your partner should never take his eyes off your face—he should actually stare at you.

While you were talking, how did you feel about the eye contact your partner was making with you?

_____

_____

Tell your partner everything you are planning to do when you get home from school until you go to sleep. While you are talking, your partner should never look at your face.

While you were talking, how did you feel about the eye contact your partner was making with you?

_____

_____

Tell your partner everything you are planning to do this weekend. While you are talking, your partner should look at you some of the time.

While you were talking, how did you feel about the eye contact your partner was making with you?

_____

_____

Facial Expressions*

Learning Objective: To teach children the difference between facial expressions; to identify possible causes for these expressions

Skill: Emotional communication, self-awareness

Ask the children, "When you look at people's faces, what do their expressions tell you?" Brainstorm ideas and write them on the blackboard or a large sheet of paper.

Tell them:

> *People's facial expressions show how they feel. The way their faces look can tell you more than what they are saying. You can often tell whether a person is angry, sad, or happy, even if you can't hear her words.*

> *When someone is talking to you, it's important for you to use an appropriate facial expression. If she is saying something funny, you would probably smile; sad, you might look serious; scary, you might have an alarmed expression on your face; and so on. If you look bored or stuck-up, that person probably won't want to continue talking with you.*

Distribute Activity Sheet 14. Children can either write in the answers or raise their hands and take turns guessing the facial expressions. Reinforce the concept that they can tell how each child is feeling even without any words being said. When asked the reason for each child's feelings, children can invent scenarios—there are no right or wrong answers.

Name ———————————————— **Date** ————————

What is this girl's facial expression saying?

_____

Why do you think she feels that way?

_____

_____

What is this boy's facial expression saying?

_____

Why do you think he feels that way?

_____

_____

What is this girl's facial expression saying?

_____

Why do you think she feels that way?

_____

_____

What is this boy's facial expression saying?

_____

Why do you think he feels that way?

_____

_____

Gestures*

Learning Objective: To teach children the meaning of gestures in nonverbal communication

Skill: Emotional communication

Ask the group what "gesture" means, and choose volunteers to show gestures with their arms and hands. Ask others to tell what they think these gestures indicate.

Tell the group:

> Gestures play an important role in communication. Many people use their hands to emphasize what they are saying. For example, clapping or giving a "thumbs up" shows your approval. Waving is a gesture of greeting or a way of saying goodbye. Other parts of the body are also used to convey the meaning of our words. Shrugging your shoulders is a way to say, "I don't know," or "I don't care."
>
> Even though we usually pay more attention to the words people are saying, it's important to recognize what signals and gestures mean so that we can communicate effectively.

Distribute Activity Sheet 15. After the children have completed it, discuss what each gesture means and when it might be used.

Name —————————————————— **Date** ——————————————————

What does this gesture mean?

_____

Describe a time this gesture might be used:

_____

_____

What does this gesture mean?

_____

Describe a time this gesture might be used:

_____

_____

What does this gesture mean?

_____

Describe a time this gesture might be used:

_____

_____

What does this gesture mean?

_____

Describe a time this gesture might be used:

_____

_____

Learning Objective: To teach children the concept of personal space

Skill: Self-awareness

Ask the children to talk about personal space. Have them focus on the word "personal" when they are thinking about the concept.

Tell them:

Personal space refers to the distance between two people. Your personal space is the space around your body that helps you feel comfortable near other people and helps them feel comfortable near you. It's like an invisible bubble you carry around with you. People who have studied personal space say that there are four space zones.

The first is called the "intimate" zone, which starts where someone can almost touch you and goes out about eighteen inches. This zone is where your family and closest friends will stand to talk with you about something personal or to be near you. If someone you don't feel close to stands in this zone, you will probably feel uncomfortable.

The second zone is called the "personal" zone. It goes from eighteen inches to four feet out from your body. People you know well stand in this zone for everyday conversations.

The third zone, the "social" zone, ranges from four to twelve feet from your body. Acquaintances stand in the social zone to talk to you.

The fourth zone is the "public" zone. It starts at twelve feet and goes as far as you can see. People stand in this zone to speak in public, for example, if someone were running for school office and had to give a speech in assembly.

Distribute Activity Sheet 16 and have children give examples of whom they would usually talk to in each zone. Besides friends and family members, they should think of people at school and in the community.

Personal Space

Name _____ Date _____

Whenever you're with another person, you should ask yourself, "Does my distance feel right?" On the lines below, write who you would feel comfortable talking to in each zone.

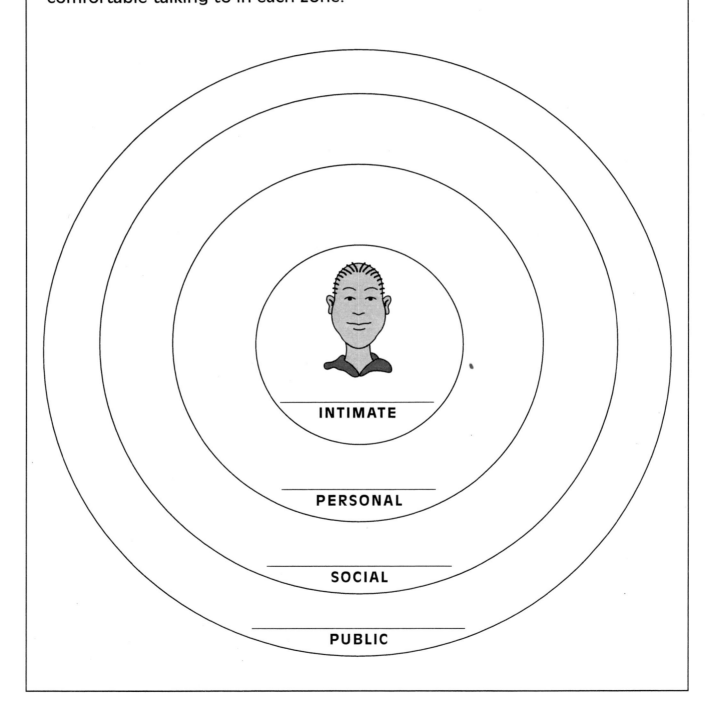

INTIMATE

PERSONAL

SOCIAL

PUBLIC

Learning Objective: To teach children the appropriate touching of others

Skill: Emotional communication, self-awareness

Tell the group:

When you touch someone appropriately, it can communicate caring, friendship, and affection. Different ways of touching have different meanings. For example, a pat on the back is usually a sign that someone else approves of what you have done; a slap tells you the opposite. Some ways of touching are acceptable, and others aren't.

There are people who are comfortable with physical contact and people who are not. Here's a good rule to remember: If someone acts as if he doesn't want to be touched, don't touch him. Some schools even have a simple "no-touch" policy during the school day; no one is allowed to touch anyone else, except during sports.

Discuss the rules about touching at school, home, and community. Then, distribute Activity Sheet 17. Children should decide whether the types of touching listed are appropriate. If they answer yes, they should choose someone whom it would be appropriate to touch in that way.

Name ——————————————— **Date** ———————————————

Decide whether the following types of touching are appropriate. If you answer yes, whom would it be appropriate to touch in that way?

	Yes	No	Whom might I touch this way?
Shaking someone's hand	☐	☐	_____
Slapping someone's face	☐	☐	_____
Giving a high-five	☐	☐	_____
Pushing in line	☐	☐	_____
Putting your arm around someone	☐	☐	_____
Holding someone's hand	☐	☐	_____
Tickling	☐	☐	_____
Poking someone in the back	☐	☐	_____
Hugging someone	☐	☐	_____
Patting someone's shoulder	☐	☐	_____
Kicking someone's leg	☐	☐	_____

Posture

Learning Objective: To teach children the meaning and messages of body posture

Skill: Emotional communication, self-awareness

Tell the group:

Your body posture can tell a lot about the way you feel in a certain situation. Standing straight might mean you feel confident or want to show respect to the other person; it could also mean you are upset or nervous. If you are slouching, your posture might tell the other person that you really don't care about what he is saying. It could also mean that you are feeling very comfortable with the person or situation, and that's why you are sitting or standing in a relaxed position.

Posture can give different messages depending on where you are. For example, slouching in your seat during class would be a sign that you were not interested or serious about your work. Slouching while you are watching TV or reading a book might just mean you are relaxed.

Have the group take turns deciding what someone's posture should be in the following situations. When they give an answer, ask them to demonstrate that posture, and tell why they think it's important to stand or sit that way. Ask them to think of additional examples.

- Listening to your teacher
- Doing your homework
- Reading
- Watching TV
- Talking with a friend on the phone
- Speaking with someone you've just met
- Eating dinner
- Waiting in the lunchroom line
- In the principal's office

Learning Objective: To help children learn about the messages our bodies give others

Skill: Emotional communication, self-awareness

Ask the group to talk about what body language is.

Tell them:

> *People can communicate messages to each other without using a single word. In fact, people are almost always doing this without realizing it. Even when they are talking, their bodies are "saying" things too.*
>
> *Body language is the unspoken communication that goes on in every encounter with another human being. It gives you clues to someone's true feelings toward you and to how well your words are being received. Experts say that 93 percent of what you are communicating comes from your body language, and only 7 percent from your words.*

Distribute Activity Sheet 19. Discuss the way the body language of each child communicates what he or she is feeling.

In a Charades type of game, children can take turns striking poses and using their bodies and facial expressions to communicate feelings, while the others guess what they are acting out.

Name _____ **Date** _____

What does the body language of these children tell you about how they feel?

This child feels _____

This child feels _____

This child feels _____

This child feels _____

Learning Objective: To recognize nonverbal signs that communicate what other people are feeling

Skill: Emotional communication, empathy

Ask the group, "How can you tell how a person is feeling?"

Tell them:

> *If you watch carefully, you can tell as much about how people are feeling from their bodies as you can from their faces. When you think you know how they are feeling, you can decide the most appropriate way to act toward them. By doing so, you can help them to feel understood and give them the message that you care about their feelings.*

Write the following emotions on the board or a large sheet of paper:

- Happy
- Angry
- Uncertain
- Disappointed
- Surprised
- Satisfied
- Confused
- Proud
- Shocked

Ask one child to choose an emotion from the list and describe a situation that might cause this emotion. Then ask other members of the group to answer these questions:

1. If a person were feeling this way, how would his face look?

2. What tone of voice would he use if he were talking?

3. What voice volume would he use?

4. What would his posture be?

5. What gestures would he use?

Learning Objective: To teach children that their appearance sends a nonverbal message to others

Skill: Emotional communication, self-awareness

Begin by telling the group to look at the clothes that they are wearing. Ask them:

> *What are some of the reasons that you picked out the clothes you are wearing today? Sometimes, there are practical reasons: you have gym class or the weather forecast predicted rain later. Maybe you chose these particular clothes because you think that what you wear is important to other people.*
>
> *How people look—their clothes, their hair, their jewelry, and even how they groom themselves—sends a message to other people.*

Have the group brainstorm what they have observed about the following people's appearances, and write their observations on the board.

- A businesswoman
- A policeman
- A teacher
- A judge
- A construction worker
- A waiter
- A popular child at school

Then, ask them to talk about what kind of messages each person's appearance gives to others.

Being Part Of A Group

Some children are socially successful with individuals, but not in groups. The inability to join a group during the elementary school years can be a very painful experience for children. Research tells us that, as they grow older, children who are social isolates are more at risk for a wide variety of problems, from academic underachievement to substance abuse. In this section, children will learn a variety of skills that can help them be accepted by groups, and even become leaders.

Group skills are particularly important in a classroom setting. Studies suggest that children's behavior in the classroom is as important to their school success as their intellectual ability is. It is only natural that teachers give more positive time and attention to children who behave well in a group. But becoming successful in a group is not an easy task. It involves many subtle skills of give-and-take, as well as the ability to assert oneself at appropriate times. And even as children learn and practice new skills, it may take a significant amount of time for them to improve their social standing in their classroom. Classrooms are essentially social groups, and all social groups form hierarchies. Once these hierarchies are established, it may be very hard for children who were previously viewed as "different" or "uncool" to change their social standing.

This fact doesn't mean, however, that such children can't be successful in a group. They simply have to find a different group—whether another group within the school or an outside group—where they are more likely to find acceptance. Studies tell us that children typically do better in groups that consist of peers who share common characteristics. Helping children identify their interests (such as computers, the environment, community service, animals, etc.) is the first step in guiding them toward joining a group of children who are more like them.

Groups of children and adults are not really the same as groups of all children, but they can still be helpful in teaching children social skills. For example, family meetings can help children learn about taking turns, respecting the opinions of others, and making suggestions. By practicing in weekly family meetings, children will become more comfortable with these skills and can eventually transfer them over to groups of their peers.

Learning Objective: To help children find ways to seek others who have similar interests; to increase group inclusion

Skill: Making friends

Ask the children to think of ways to find groups they might like to join. Suggest that they focus on their individual interests. Brainstorm ideas and write them on the blackboard or a large sheet of paper.

Tell them:

> *Throughout their lives, people participate in many different kinds of social groups: scout troops, faith-based groups, sports teams, clubs, and more. A class is also a kind of group. Your classmates are part of your group experience every day at school. Some children are also in specialized classes, such as art, computer, music, and science classes that meet after school or on weekends. A child's life—and an adult's, too—is filled with different kinds of groups.*

Distribute Activity Sheet 22. Children can write the answers or raise their hands and answer the questions aloud. Use their responses as the basis for a discussion about the different aspects of joining a group.

Joining A Group

Name —————————————————————— Date ——————————

Matt has just moved to the neighborhood and is a new student at school. He is sitting at a lunch table where a group of kids are planning some activities for the weekend. He wants to be included but doesn't know what to do.

What could Matt do to become part of the group?

_____

Do you think Matt should speak first or wait until someone in the group speaks to him?

_____

What could Matt say to start a conversation?

_____

Should the group invite Matt to join them? Why or why not?

_____

Tell about a time when you had a hard time connecting with people in a group. How did you feel? What did you do?

_____

_____

_____

Learning Objective: To teach children the basics of building and enhancing relationships with peers

Skill: Making friends

Ask the group, "What would you do if there were someone you'd like to be friends with?" Brainstorm ideas and write them on the blackboard or a large sheet of paper.

Tell them:

> *Most people want to be friends with others, but meeting new people isn't always easy. It takes time to get to know another person.*
>
> *The first step is starting a conversation. Try to think of something the other person might be interested in—something the two of you might both have experienced, such as, "Did you watch the baseball game last night?" or "Can you believe how much math homework we got?" Once you begin a conversation, the other person will usually join in, and you'll be on your way to forming a friendship. When you feel comfortable with the other person, you can usually plan to do something together.*

Call on volunteers to talk about their friendships—old or new—and how they developed. Ask them to try to remember everything they did to build these friendships.

Then, pair children who don't know each other well. Tell them to talk with each other to find out what they have in common—what they each like to do and why, their families, their pets, their favorite subjects in school, and so on. Each pair can then share what they have learned about each other with the group.

Learning Objective: To understand the importance of asking questions during a conversation

Skill: Social communication

Tell the group:

> *Asking questions is the best way to get as much information about a subject as possible. When you ask questions you show that you are interested in other people and you keep the conversation going. You will also learn things from people's answers that will make you a better friend.*

For practice, have the children turn to the person on their right. One of the two people secretly focuses on something in the room (e.g., the clock) and gives a clue, such as, "I'm thinking of something on the wall." The other person asks questions (e.g., "What color is it?" or "Which wall is it on?") until she guesses the object.

Distribute Activity Sheet 24 and have the same pairs of children practice asking questions.

Name _____ **Date** _____

Here's the beginning of a conversation you and your partner can have. After you have read your parts, keep the conversation going by making up three more questions and answers.

You: I have a dog. **Your partner:** What's his name?

You: Dusty **Your partner:** What kind of dog is he?

You: A golden retriever **Your partner:** _____

You: _____ **Your partner:** _____

You: _____ **Your partner:** _____

You: _____

Next, your partner should tell you everything he learned about Dusty, beginning with "You have a dog named Dusty..."

Now, switch the order. Your partner starts the conversation by saying, "I have a friend." When five questions have been asked and answered, it's your turn to tell your partner what you learned about his friend, beginning with "You have a friend..."

Learning Objective: To teach children to understand the value of sharing with others

Skill: Empathy, social interaction

Ask the group to brainstorm about sharing. Do they think sharing can be difficult? If so, why? Might the outcome of any situation be better if they share? Why?

Tell the children:

> *Learning to share is hard for a lot of children, because it means giving something up. But it also means being generous and thinking about the needs of others. When you share, you feel good because you are being nice to someone else. When someone shares with you, you feel good because they are being considerate to you.*

Present the following examples to the group, one at a time. After each, ask the children whether it would be easy or hard for them to share in the situation. Encourage them to talk about what they would do, and why.

- The whole group is reading a book, and there aren't enough copies to go around.

- There's only one brownie left on the plate.

- Three people are sitting on a sofa, and the fourth person has nowhere to sit.

Ask the group to think of other examples when sharing is necessary.

Learning Objective: To teach children the meaning and importance of cooperating to achieve a common goal

Skill: Social interaction

Ask the group, "What does it mean to cooperate with another person?"

Tell them:

When people cooperate, they work together toward a common goal or something they want to achieve. For example, they might cooperate to get a school project done, or to do something they enjoy in their free time together.

When you cooperate, you save time by putting your heads together. You can also have more fun, because you are interacting with someone and getting to know that person. In the end, when people cooperate, they usually both feel good about working together.

Encourage the group to think of situations when they had to cooperate with another person. Ask them:

- What are some ways you cooperate at school?

- What are some ways you cooperate at home?

- What are some ways you cooperate when you play a game or sport?

- What might happen if one person in a group didn't cooperate?

- What could you do if one person in a group didn't cooperate?

If time allows, divide the group into pairs. With a piece of rope, loosely tie the right ankle of one person in each pair to the left ankle of the other. Have them walk across the room together, reminding them that they have to cooperate to get to their goal.

Following Rules

Learning Objective: To teach children that some rules are inflexible, while other rules can be changed

Skill: Respect, creating consensus

Ask the group, "What does it mean to follow rules? What would happen if people didn't follow them?" Brainstorm ideas and write them on the blackboard or a large sheet of paper.

Tell them:

> *Rules tell us how to behave. Some rules should always be followed so that people don't get hurt or have something bad happen. "Don't steal," "Don't cheat," and "Tell the truth" are all rules that should always be followed. In a group like this one, there are certain rules that we follow so that everyone can get along. Some of the rules are: don't interrupt others, don't use bad language, and don't say things that will be hurtful to others. If we didn't have these rules, it would be very hard for us to get along.*

> *Other rules are more flexible. If your bedtime is 9:30, your mom might "bend" the rule and let you stay up later sometimes. Rules can only be bent if no one gets hurt or suffers as a result. In our group, we have certain rules that are more flexible too. For example, if we do an activity that people don't like, we may be able to change it the net time.*

Ask the children which of the following rules must always be kept and which can be changed sometimes. Have them give the reasons for their choices.

- Don't hit anyone in anger.
- Eat a balanced meal.

- Keep your room neat.
- Don't talk behind people's backs.

- Listen to the teacher.
- Make your bed every morning.

Children can offer other rules from home and school, and tell why these rules should always be kept or can sometimes be bent.

Learning Objective: To teach children to weigh options and make decisions as a group

Skill: Creating consensus

Divide the children into groups of three or four. Choose a spokesperson and a note-taker for each group.

Tell them:

> *Your group has just been given a large sum of money to use for any purpose it chooses. You could donate it to a charity, you could go on a shopping spree, you could use it for school supplies—you can decide to do anything you want with it, but you must come to the decision together.*

Give each group 15 minutes to brainstorm ideas, which the note-taker writes down. Each person should try to persuade the group by telling why she feels her idea is the most sensible, fun, altruistic, and so on.

At the end of the 15-minute period, the group must decide on one idea. If they don't succeed in deciding, they will "lose" the money. Each group's spokesperson then tells the larger group of their decision, and each group member must say why he thinks it's a good idea, even if it wasn't his idea originally.

For example, one child might say, "I originally thought we should donate the money to a charity. When the group decided to buy toys for kids who don't get holiday gifts, I realized doing that is kind of the same thing," or "I originally thought we should donate it to a charity. When the group decided we should take a vacation together, I realized that would be more fun. I can still donate some of my own money to a charity."

Being A Good Sport

Learning Objective: To teach children that being a "good sport" will help them get along better with others

Skill: Social interaction

Ask the group, "What does it mean to be a 'good sport'?" Brainstorm ideas and write them on the blackboard or a large sheet of paper.

Tell them:

> Being a good sport when you're playing a game is important. It's also important to be a good sport when things don't go exactly the way you want, or expect, them to.
>
> Suppose you don't get chosen for a team, or you get the worst-looking piece of cake on the plate, or you get hit with a ball by accident. If you can accept that things like that happen from time to time—that no one is out to get you—you'll be considered a good sport.
>
> It's okay to be upset if things don't go your way, but it's best to save your hurt or anger for a time when it's safe and appropriate to express those feelings—probably to someone who cares about you and will understand. In the meantime, it will help you get along with others if you can accept what happens and be pleasant about it.

Have the group volunteer to tell about circumstances when something they wanted to happen didn't go according to plan. How did they react? Did things go more smoothly when they were good sports?

Fostering Group Identity

Learning Objective: To foster cohesiveness through the development of group identity

Skill: Social interaction

Tell the group, "Even though some of you are boys and some are girls, and even though you have different backgrounds, you still have things in common with each other."

Explain that:

All groups are based on things the members have in common, like shared interests. For example, there are clubs whose members all plant gardens or collect trading cards. There are community service groups that were formed because all the members wanted to help other people. Even though these groups are made up of many different kinds of people, each person has at least one thing in common with everyone else in the group.

These common interests are the basis for your group's identity. When a group has an identity, you have a feeling of importance and belonging. Just like having good feelings about yourself, you can have good feelings about your group. These feelings can make you proud and happy to be part of your group.

Groups have different ways of expressing their identity. These include: the name of the group, a uniform or something that every group member wears, a symbol that represents the group, or even a secret handshake!

Divide the group into pairs, and ask each pair to make up a simple, easy-to-remember handshake or other gesture for group members to use when they meet. Each pair should present their idea to the group, and then the group can vote on the one they like best.

Accepting Differences*

Learning Objective: To promote appreciation of individual differences

Skill: Social interaction

Ask the group to explain the word "diversity."

Say to them:

> *To get along with other people, it's necessary to be tolerant of the ways they are different from you. Our world is made up of people from many different cultures, races, and backgrounds. We all want to be liked and treated well, and stereotypes and prejudice only foster bad feelings. If we respect each other's differences, we can all learn from each other.*
>
> *No matter how different people look or act, we must always be kind to them. It takes time to really get to know people—beyond the way they look, talk, or act. And think about it: wouldn't the world be a boring place if everyone were the same?*

Distribute Activity Sheet 31, and divide the group into pairs. Seated face-to-face, they should draw each other's face and hair in the space provided on the activity sheet. When they have completed the activity, lead a discussion about the noticeable differences and similarities within the group.

Name _____ Date _____

In the space below, draw your partner's face and hair. Then, tell three ways you are different from each other and three ways you are similar.

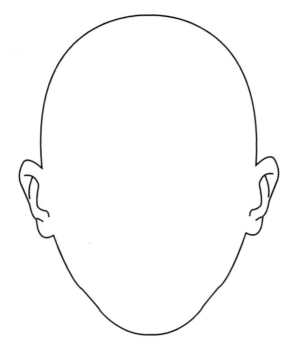

Here are three ways my partner and I are different:

1._____

2._____

3._____

Here are three ways we are similar:

1._____

2._____

3._____

My Role Model

Learning Objective: To identify positive qualities of role models

Skill: Self-awareness

Ask, "What is a 'role model'?" Brainstorm ideas and write them on the blackboard or a large sheet of paper.

Tell the group:

> Role models are people you really admire. You may like their values, the way they live their lives, and the things that are important to them. You may look up to them. You may even want to be just like them.
>
> Most people's role models are famous people—celebrities, sports stars, politicians, and so on. In this activity, try to think of someone you know personally who is really terrific. It could be a parent, teacher, or friend. It might be someone you know casually whom you think is really cool.

Ask for volunteers to talk about their role models. Encourage them by asking these questions:

- What has that person done to become your role model?

- Does your role model help others? How?

- What's the most important quality a role model should have?

- What could you do to be like your role model?

Learning Objective: To teach children that having true friends is more important than being in a "popular" group

Skill: Making friends

Ask the group, "What does it mean to be popular in your school?"

Tell them:

Sometimes, children really want to be part of a popular group. When they get to know the children in that group, they often find that they don't like them very much. Just being in a specific group of children doesn't make you happy; having friends who care about you and treat you well does.

With this idea in mind, think about your true friends. Do they like you? Do they accept you? Do they admire you? The answer to these questions is probably yes. As long as you have true friends, it doesn't matter whether your group is considered to be popular or not.

Hand out Activity Sheet 33. After the children complete the sheet, have them share their answers.

Name ——————————————— Date ———————————————

Thinking about a good friend, complete this sheet. If you want to, you can give the completed sheet to your friend.

My friend likes me because _____.

I like my friend because _____.

My friend's favorite thing to do is _____.

My friend and I like to _____ together.

My friend admires me because _____.

My friend is really great because _____.

Two things my friend and I have in common are _____

and _____.

Here's a picture of my friend:

Learning Objective: To help children understand the negatives of being in a clique

Skill: Making friends

Ask the group to share their ideas about what a clique is. Do they think there are cliques in their school?

Tell them:

> A clique is a group made up of friends who may look and act the same way. Usually, clique members don't like to let other people into their group which makes other kids consider them snobby or stuck-up. One important thing to remember is that those in the clique are probably trying really hard to fit in and keep up with being part of the group. They have to be cool and always do whatever the clique considers the right thing. Often, they have to dress and look alike, which can put a lot of pressure on them. If they can't keep up, they may get kicked out of the clique.
>
> If you're not in a clique and you want to be, keep in mind that there's no reason to limit your friendships. In the long run, it's better to have a diverse group of friends from whom you can learn different things and with whom you can have different experiences.

Ask three or four children to sit in the middle of the group and act like a clique talking about their favorite movie or TV show. As volunteers try to join the conversation, clique members should continue to exclude them. After about ten minutes, have the clique rejoin the main group. Then, have a discussion about how it felt to be in the clique and how it felt to be excluded.

Expressing Your Feelings

Children who are able to talk about their feelings are typically viewed as more interesting by their peers and more likable by adults. If they do not express their feelings because they are shy, children are often viewed as standoffish, or even unimportant. Those who act out their feelings, rather than talking about them, are frequently seen as impulsive or aggressive. Helping children learn to express, accept, and control their feelings will benefit them in all their relationships.

The ability to express feelings is also an important factor in a child's emotional development. Research on emotional intelligence (see *How to Raise a Child with a High EQ*, by the author, Quill, 1998) correlates this ability with both social and academic success.

This section includes activities that will help children express their feelings and also control them. Anger control is a skill that is particularly important to social success. Angry children are often ostracized by their peers and viewed by teachers as behavior problems. Often, children with problems in anger control find themselves in a negative cycle of social defeat. The more that they express their anger in inappropriate ways, the more negative feedback they receive, which in turn causes more anger and resentment.

Teaching children to express and control their feelings will not only help them win more immediate social approval, but will also help them develop the emotional foundation for success as teens, and even as adults. Many psychologists think that emotional and social skills learned in childhood form the foundation for developing intimate relationships in later life.

Learning Objective: To define feelings a person might experience at different times; to increase recognition of these feelings

Skill: Emotional awareness

Write the four groups of feelings in this activity on the blackboard or a large sheet of paper. Ask the group, "What are some feelings you might have during a normal day?"

Tell them:

Everyone experiences many different feelings and emotions. Some are sad feelings, some are angry, some are happy, and others are scared feelings. They are all a little different. For example,

When you're SAD, you might feel:
Discouraged
Depressed
Unhappy
Hurt
Uncomfortable
Embarrassed

Some HAPPY feelings might be:
Excited
Cheerful
Confident
Comfortable
Proud
Satisfied

Some ANGRY feelings might be:
Threatened
Disgusted
Frustrated
Jealous
Resentful

When you're SCARED, you might feel:
Terrified
Nervous
Anxious
Confused
Unsure

Distribute Activity Sheet 35. When the children have finished, show them several examples of completed sheets and ask the group to identify the feelings. Then, ask them to demonstrate one of the feelings they chose to draw.

Identifying Feelings

Name —————————————————————— Date ——————————————

Choose one feeling from each of the four categories—SAD, HAPPY, ANGRY and SCARED—and draw a face showing that feeling.

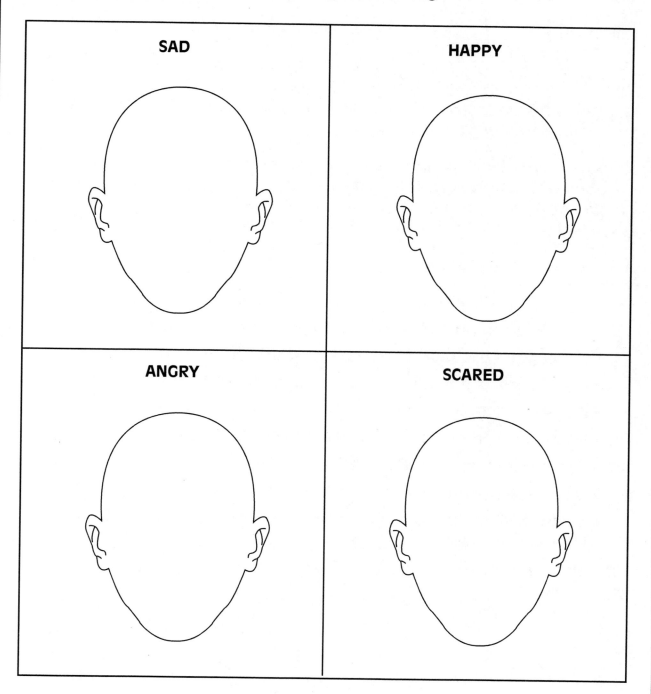

SAD

HAPPY

ANGRY

SCARED

Learning Objective: To teach children that expressing their feelings can help in dealing with them

Skill: Emotional communication

Tell the group:

It's important to recognize how you are feeling at different times and to express your feelings appropriately. If you're angry, it's better to tell someone than to keep it inside. If you're happy, it's hard to keep your excitement to yourself.

Expressing your feelings will help you deal with them. Telling someone you trust and sharing your feelings in a conversation almost always makes you feel better. When you're aware of what you feel, it is usually easier for you to get along with others.

Ask different children to tell how they would feel in the situations below, and why.

- If your mom were angry at you for not doing your chores
- If you got a bad grade on a test you had studied for
- If you got a bad grade on a test you hadn't studied for
- If you got 100% on a test
- If your best friend couldn't come to your birthday party
- If you lost your homework
- If someone teased you
- If your teacher called on you to answer a question, and you didn't know the answer

Then, have the children think of their own examples, and again tell how they would feel, and why.

I-Messages*   ACTIVITY 37

Learning Objective: To teach children the use of I-messages to express themselves without placing blame

Skill: Emotional communication

Ask the group, "What is an 'I-message'?"

Tell them:

> When you're angry with people, it's easy to blame them for whatever happened. But when you blame other people, they often get angry with you. Then, everyone ends up with hurt feelings. You can use I-messages to tell other people what you really want, without judging, confronting, or blaming them. You can also use I-messages to express other feelings, like happiness or fear. I-messages always focus on what the speaker feels, rather than blaming the listener.
>
> Here's how an I-message works:
>
> 1. Say what you feel (I FEEL...)
> 2. Tell what the other person did that upset you (WHEN YOU...)
> 3. Describe how you were affected (BECAUSE...)
> 4. State what would make the situation better for you (AND I WANT...)
>
> For example, let's imagine that Megan told Sara a secret, which Sara then told Kevin. Megan is very angry, so she tells Sara:
>
> "I FEEL angry WHEN YOU tell my secret BECAUSE I asked you not to AND I WANT you to apologize and never do that again."

Distribute Activity Sheet 37. Pairs of children can take turns stating their I-messages to each other. These I-messages can be based on real or imagined situations. Individual children can also complete the sheet on their own.

Name _____ Date _____

Complete these I-messages for practice. Then, make up two of your own.

I FEEL ___*happy*___ WHEN YOU _____

BECAUSE _____ AND I WANT _____.

I FEEL ___*frustrated*___ WHEN YOU _____

BECAUSE _____ AND I WANT _____.

I FEEL ___*afraid*___ WHEN YOU _____

BECAUSE _____ AND I WANT _____.

I FEEL ___*sad*___ WHEN YOU _____

BECAUSE _____ AND I WANT _____.

I FEEL ___mad___ WHEN YOU _____

BECAUSE _____ AND I WANT _____.

I FEEL ___happy___ WHEN YOU _____

BECAUSE _____ AND I WANT _____.

Learning Objective: To teach children how to identify with, and understand, another person's feelings

Skill: Empathy

Ask the group what it means to "put yourself in another person's shoes." Encourage them to share examples from their own experience.

Tell them:

> When you put yourself in another person's shoes, you empathize with her. Empathy is the ability to understand another person's feelings as if they were your own. When we see and feel things the way other people do, we can get along better with them.

> People who have empathy for others can feel sad with them, or happy for them, and so on. They know what it is like to feel that way. When children can understand another person's point of view and respect her feelings, they are less likely to start fights and more likely to make friends easily. They are better liked by other children and more successful in school.

Distribute Activity Sheet 38. In a discussion, the children can take turns choosing from the examples on the sheet, and/or telling about times wheh they empathized with others.

Name _____ **Date** _____

How do you think Allie felt when Brianne didn't invite her to her party?

_____

Can you empathize with Allie?

_____

Did anything like this ever happen to you?_____

How do you think Joe felt when he wasn't picked for the team?

_____

Can you empathize with Joe?

_____

Did anything like this ever happen to you?_____

How do you think Kate's mom felt when Kate ignored her? _____

Can you empathize with Kate's mom?

_____

Did anything like this ever happen to you?_____

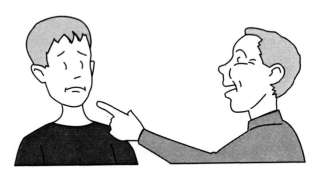

How do you think Sharif felt when Kyle teased him?_____

Can you empathize with Sharif?

_____

Did anything like this ever happen to you?_____

Learning Objective: To teach children that people often have more than one feeling at the same time

Skill: Emotional awareness

Tell the group:

People can have more than one emotion at the same time. For example, you might feel happy when your lost dog comes home, but upset because he has a bruised paw. You could feel excited about finding the last piece of cake in the refrigerator, but unsure about whether you should eat it.

The important thing is to try to be aware of all the emotions you're feeling, and if they trouble you, talk about them with someone who will listen to you and can help.

Distribute Activity Sheet 39. When the children have completed it, ask for volunteers to talk about situations in which they had mixed feelings.

Name _____ Date _____

For each situation below, what feelings might you have?

I feel _____

I also feel _____

My mom just had a new baby.

I feel _____

I also feel _____

Our school trip was cancelled, and it was supposed to be the same day that my favorite cousin will be visiting from out of town.

I feel _____

I also feel _____

My friend broke my new CD player but she is going to get it fixed.

I feel _____

I also feel _____

I got a great gift for my birthday but it wasn't what I was hoping for.

Self-Talk*

Learning Objective: To teach children to use positive self-talk to direct their thoughts and behavior

Skill: Emotional control

Ask the group, "What is self-talk?" Prompt them to think of the two words— "self" and "talk"— separately.

Tell them:

> Self-talk is what you say to yourself every minute of every day. It's also called "inner speech." You're probably not aware of it, but you are constantly telling yourself things that affect what you think, say, and do. For example, if you are afraid, you can say to yourself, "It's okay, there is nothing to worry about." You can help yourself concentrate by saying something like, "Tune everything else out, and focus on what you are doing."

> If you think positively, you will probably succeed. If you think in negative terms, you probably won't. When you recognize the thoughts that make you feel good, you can make them happen more often. Some people write their positive thoughts down and read them during the day. Other people just try and repeat the positive thoughts at different times during the day, until thinking these thoughts becomes a habit. You can learn to comfort yourself when things go wrong. You can learn to be your own best friend!

Distribute Activity Sheet 40. After the children complete it, have them discuss how positive self-talk really does make people feel better about themselves.

Name ———————————————— Date ————————

Read the statements below. For each, give an example of negative self-talk. Then, replace it with positive self-talk.

There's a math test on Friday. I'm going to fail—no doubt about it.

NEGATIVE SELF-TALK

There's a math test on Friday. If I study hard, I'll do okay.

POSITIVE SELF-TALK

I really want a puppy.

Negative self-talk: _____

Positive self-talk: _____

I wish I were taller.

Negative self-talk: _____

Positive self-talk: _____

Kayla's clothes are so cool.

Negative self-talk: _____

Positive self-talk: _____

Learning Objective: To teach children the importance of remaining calm under stress and controlling impulsive behavior

Skill: Emotional control, self-control

Ask the group, "What is self-control?" Brainstorm ideas and write them on the blackboard or a large sheet of paper.

Tell them:

> *When you have self-control, you decide the best way to act instead of acting without thinking. It might only take a second or two, but a person with self-control stops, thinks, and remains calm—even if she is very upset or angry. Before she acts, she thinks about the situation and what might happen if she reacts impulsively.*

Ask for volunteers to talk about the following situations, stopping first to think about what they would do to exercise self-control.

- Someone hits you on the arm.
- You get chocolate all over your new shirt.
- Your sister forgets to close the door and your dog runs away.
- You get a D on a test you studied hard for.
- Your parents cancel a vacation you were looking forward to.
- You have no idea how to do your math homework.

Ask the group to think of recent situations in which they were upset or angry. Have them tell about what they did, and whether they exercised self-control or reacted impulsively.

Learning Objective: To teach children to deal with anger in peaceful, verbal, and nonphysical ways

Skill: Emotional control

Ask the group, "What does it feel like to be angry?" and/or "What makes you angry?"

Tell them:

> *Everyone gets angry, and dealing with your own angry feelings isn't easy. First, you have to recognize "triggers," or things that make you angry. You have to know why you are angry. When you are aware of these triggers, you can learn to stay calm and in control. You can learn to deal with your anger peacefully, using words, thoughts, and nonthreatening actions instead of physical means.*

Distribute Activity Sheet 42. Have the children fill it out and share their experiences and choices of constructive ways to manage their anger.

Name —————————————————— **Date** ——————————

Think of a recent situation in which you were angry and didn't manage your anger well. What happened? How did you react? Write about it here:

———————————————————————————————

———————————————————————————————

———————————————————————————————

———————————————————————————————

Now choose a sign that would have helped you deal with your anger in a more constructive way, and fill in the blank.

IT'S NO BIG DEAL BECAUSE

——————————

——————————

I'LL TAKE A DEEP BREATH AND I'LL FEEL

——————————

——————————

I CAN KEEP CALM BY

——————————

——————————

——————————

I'M WALKING AWAY, AND THAT MAKES ME FEEL

——————————

——————————

——————————

I CAN THINK OF SOMETHING ELSE, LIKE

——————————

——————————

I CAN TALK ABOUT MY ANGER WITH

——————————

Learning Objective: To teach children to deal with another person's anger in a constructive, nonthreatening manner

Skill: Coping

Ask the group, "Have you ever had to deal with another person's anger? Was it hard to know what to do?" As children offer their insights and reactions, write them on the blackboard or a large sheet of paper.

Tell them:

When someone is angry with you, it's easy to become angry yourself. But it's important to remain calm, listen to what the person is saying, respond in a quiet voice, and even try to negotiate or explain your point of view.

Wait until the person is finished talking and ask why he is angry. Doing that will help him sort out his feelings, and he may even find that he's not really angry with you—maybe he's just taking his anger out on you. But what if he is actually angry with you? After listening to his answer you can either apologize (if you agree that you did something wrong) or talk about what happened and give your point of view (if you don't). If you find yourself losing control and becoming angry, you should walk away for a while, saying something like "We're both angry now. Let's talk about this later."

Distribute Activity Sheet 43. Choose two children to role-play each scenario. After the role-plays are completed, discuss the differences between the angry confrontations and the modified versions. Ask how each child felt in each version.

Role-play this scenario for the group.
Leigh: Hey, you stepped on my foot!
Marie: I did? I didn't realize it.
Leigh: Are you kidding? It really hurts!
Marie: Hey, I said I didn't realize it!

Role-play this modified scenario for the group.
Leigh: Hey, you stepped on my foot!
Marie: I did? I didn't realize it.
Leigh: Well, it hurt.
Marie: I'm sorry. I didn't mean to step on your
foot.
Leigh: That's okay.

Role-play this scenario for the group.
Sarah: I'm so mad. I got a D on my test.
Jake: I got an A.
Sarah: How did you get an A? That's not fair!
Jake: I studied hard and it paid off.
Sarah: That's still not fair!
Jake: Oh well, there's nothing you can do about
it now, can you?

Role-play this modified scenario for the group.
Sarah: I'm so mad. I got a D on my test.
Jake: I got an A.
Sarah: Really? How'd you do that?
Jake: I studied really hard. Next time we can
study together if you want.
Sarah: That would be great. Thanks.

Learning Objective: To teach children to accept change in their lives, whether good or bad

Skill: Coping, emotional control

Ask whether anyone in the group has ever experienced a major change in life, involving family, friends, school, or something else. Have the children who respond share how they reacted to these changes. As children offer their answers, write them on the blackboard or a large sheet of paper.

Tell them:

Change is hard to accept. Just when you think things are going great, your parents decide to move, or get divorced, or have a new baby. Things like that happen in life, and they can make you feel happiness, sadness, or many other feelings. It's frustrating sometimes, because you can't control many changes in life.

If you can learn to accept change, you'll be better prepared for the changes that will come throughout your life. You can decide what's good or bad about each change, and eventually you will adjust to it.

Activity Sheet 44 deals with small changes of plan. Although changes like these may not have great impact on a child's life, they are disturbing nevertheless. As children learn to deal with such small changes, they also develop the coping skills to deal with changes that have a more significant impact. Have the children tell how they would feel in each situation, and how they would adjust to the change of plans.

Name ——————————————————— **Date** ———————————————

How would you feel in each situation? How could you handle the change in a way that would help?

Our class trip has been cancelled because we have so much work to get done.

I would feel _____.

I could _____

_____.

You'll have to wear your old jacket because your new one is dirty.

I would feel _____.

I could _____

_____.

I know I said I'd go to the movies with you, but I forgot I told Matt I'd do something with him today.

I would feel _____.

I could _____

_____.

I have to work late today so I won't be able to come to your game.

I would feel _____.

I could _____

_____.

Caring About Yourself And Others

Caring and kindness are important values in our culture, and they are virtues that are the underpinning of a child's moral development. According to Brown University Professor William Damon, a leading expert on the moral development of children, elementary school age children should be able to:

- Understand what distinguishes "good" from "bad" behavior and develop habits of conduct that are consistent with what they perceive as "good."

- Develop concern, regard, and a sense of responsibility for the welfare and rights of others, and express this concern in acts of caring, benevolence, and kindness.

- Experience negative emotional reactions, including shame, guilt, outrage, fear, and contempt for breaking moral rules.

The desire to care for and about others, even to the point of self-sacrifice, is part of our genetic coding. We can observe altruistic behavior in children as young as two years of age. By age six, children should begin to take the perspective of others. By age twelve, they should expand their empathy beyond people they know and begin to show concern for abstract causes—such as the environment or saving whales—as well as for people whom they will never know.

Yet even the casual observer of children in today's culture would question whether or not this altruism is happening. According to one survey, nearly 80% of adults say that children today are ruder and less respectful than children of previous generations.

Many people blame such behavior on negative messages in the mass media, and the cultural emphasis on self-centered behavior. Others point to the change in today's families and the decreasing amount of time that parents spend with their children. Whatever the cause, if we want children to be kind, cooperative, and empathetic, simply talking about values is clearly not enough—we must teach them these values both at home and at school. The activities in this section are designed for children to experience the positive feelings that go along with behaviors that reflect a concern for others.

Learning Objective: To help children understand that it's okay to ask for help when they need it

Skill: Social communication

Ask the group to volunteer how they feel about asking for help. Explain that asking for help is part of being responsible to—or taking care of—themselves. Ask them to think of situations where they might need help. Brainstorm ideas and write them on the blackboard or a large sheet of paper.

Tell them:

It's always okay to ask for help. You should never be embarrassed or worry about what others will think. Instead, you should think about what would happen if you don't get help. That could be worse!

Always remember that anyone you ask for help will probably be very happy you asked, and very happy to help you. People like to feel needed.

Here are the steps to remember when you think you need help from an adult:

- *Decide what the problem is.*
- *Decide what help you think you need.*
- *Decide if you really do need help or if you can solve the problem yourself. Remember, it's okay if you do need help!*
- *Think of whom you can ask for help. This person will probably be someone you trust and who will know how to help you.*
- *Think about what you'll say.*
- *Tell the person your problem and ask for help.*

Distribute Activity Sheet 45. After the children have filled in the speech balloons, talk about their responses.

Name _____ **Date** _____

This child is asking for help with a problem, and the adult is giving some helpful advice. In the speech balloons, write what they are saying.

Learning Objective: To teach children how their behavior affects others

Skill: Empathy

Ask the group to think about a time when another person's behavior affected them in an important way.

Substituting names of children in the group, say:

> *For example, if Dana distracted Michael so that he couldn't hear what I was saying, Michael wouldn't know what tomorrow's homework is. In fact, neither child would know. This is a simple example, but there are many things people do that affect others in both positive and negative ways.*

Distribute Activity Sheet 46. After the children have completed the sheet, have them discuss the situations and reasons why they chose "positive" or "negative" for each example.

Name _____ Date _____

For each example, think about whether the first person's behavior would have a positive or negative impact on the second person. Then put a check in the correct column. Use the blank spaces to write your own examples.

	Positive Impact	Negative Impact
Darla takes Harry's lunch without asking.	_____	_____
Leslie shares her glitter markers with Jason.	_____	_____
Barry returns a book that Ian lost.	_____	_____
Ryan cheats by looking at Paul's test paper.	_____	_____
Olivia shakes her leg in class and it distracts Rudy.	_____	_____
Mark laughs when Todd falls off his bike.	_____	_____
Ayisha helps Tamara with her homework.	_____	_____
Nancy teases Jodie on the playground.	_____	_____
_____	_____	_____
_____	_____	_____

Learning Objective: To teach children ways to better understand why people behave the way they do

Skill: Empathy

Ask the group if they have ever wondered why people act the way they do. Have them think of times when they wondered why someone acted in a particular way, which may have differed from the way they would have acted.

As children offer their answers and insights, write them on the blackboard or a large sheet of paper.

Explain that:

> *No two people are exactly alike. Everyone sees things differently, and no one can really know how another person views something. To understand the behavior of others, it's best to:*

> - *Listen to what the other person is saying.*
>
> - *Watch what he's doing.*
>
> - *Think of reasons why he's saying or doing those things. (If you don't know, ask him.)*
>
> - *Decide which reason explains his behavior best.*

> *Then, decide if you have to say or do anything in response. Follow through by doing what you think is best.*

Then, have children who are familiar with each other pair up. The first child should describe something the second child did recently—what he had for lunch, what he's wearing, or anything about his individual behavior. He can then talk about why he thinks the person behaved that way and/or ask the person about it.

Caring About Others*

Learning Objective: To teach children to think about and practice ways of caring for others

Skill: Empathy

Ask the group, "Who is a special person you care about? Why do you care about this person?" As children volunteer names and reasons, write them on the blackboard or a large sheet of paper.

Explain that:

> *One of the best gifts you can give people is to let them know that you care about them. When you help people, show concern for them, or say something nice, you show them that you care. When you listen to them, share something, or laugh about something together, you show them that you care. And when you show people that you really care, you can make their day!*

Distribute Activity Sheet 48A. When the group has completed it, have children share experiences they have had caring about, and for, others. Then hand out Activity Sheet 48B, and have them write notes to special people with whom they have caring relationships.

Name ———————————————— Date ————————

Draw a line to connect each person on the left to the child who is acting in a caring way.

Name ———————————————————————— **Date** ————————————

Dear ———————————————————————

I care about you because ————————————————————

———————————————————————————————————

———————————————————————————————————

———————————————————————————————————

———————————————————————————————————

———————————————————————————————————

———————————————————————————————————

From, ————————————————————

Learning Objective: To teach children how to show that they are interested in other people

Skill: Social communication

Ask the group what they would do to show interest in another person. Brainstorm ideas and write them on the blackboard or a large sheet of paper.

Tell them:

When someone pays attention to you, it makes you feel like you're a person worth listening to. When you speak in a friendly and polite way to others, you are showing interest in what they are telling you. Showing interest in what others say and do helps build trust and caring.

Distribute Activity Sheet 49. After the children complete it, talk about the responses they wrote in the speech balloons.

Name _____ Date _____

By asking what kind of soup Lisa had, Michael is showing interest in her. What can each person below say to show interest in the other person?

> I had soup for lunch today.

> What kind of soup?

> I had such a busy day!

> I didn't get the part.

> I got this tie for my birthday.

> I like strawberry better than vanilla.

Learning Objective: To teach children the importance of behaving in ways that help others

Skill: Helpfulness

Begin by asking the group what they think "prosocial behavior" means.

Tell them:

> *Prosocial behavior is any action a person takes to help another person. It includes sharing, helping, protecting, comforting, showing affection, and giving encouragement. It always involves giving up something—like time, safety, or even concrete things like money—for the good of someone else.*
>
> *Here are some examples of prosocial things you can do for another person:*
> - *Saying something to cheer her up*
> - *If he is in pain, reminding him of the good things in his life*
> - *Listening to her talk about what's bothering her without judging*
> - *Reassuring him that it's okay to feel angry or sad*
> - *Reminding her that it's okay to express her emotions*
> - *Helping him figure out what to do to make a situation better*
>
> *Many people find that the more they give—the more they practice prosocial behavior—the better they feel just from the act of giving.*

Ask the group to give examples of times when they were prosocial toward another person. Make sure they tell how they felt afterwards.

Learning Objective: To recognize and promote positive acts of kindness; to teach children that being kind to others is its own reward

Skill: Empathy

Ask children to define "kindness." Following their responses, tell them:

We demonstrate kindness when we treat each other with love, dignity and respect, without expecting anything in return. Kindness is like "love in action."

Give several examples of kind things people do for each other.

At least once a week, designate time for children and teachers to share stories of kindness from their daily lives. Have children draw pictures about their kindness stories and share them with others. After sharing, talk about how kindness makes both the giver and recipient feel. Discuss why kindness is important in friendships and families.

Copy Activity Sheet 51 as many times as needed so that there is one heart for each child. Cut out the hearts, and put a child's name on each one. Put all the hearts in a basket or bag, and have the children close their eyes as they choose a heart with another child's name. On the other side of the heart, ask them to write something kind or nice they could do for that child. After they have completed the activity, have the children read aloud what they wrote on their hearts.

Kindness Cards

Learning Objective: To teach children the importance of doing a kind act each day

Skill: Empathy

At the top of a large index card, write the words "Kindness Card." Then draw one circle on the card for each member of the group.

Say to the group:

> I want you to do something kind for someone else in the group while we meet today. The first person to do something kind gets to put her initials in a circle on the card. Then she should give the Kindness Card to someone else, who must do something kind for another group member and pass the card to another person. By the end the week, everyone's initials should be on the card.

During the group meeting, talk about how simple it is to do a kind act at least once a day. Make a list of kindnesses that children can do, such as:

- Hold the door for someone.

- Make a phone call to a grandparent.

- Give someone a compliment.

- Volunteer to do a chore at home or in the classroom.

As a follow-up, you can give each group member a Kindness Card with seven circles to take along with them. Challenge them to do a kind act each day for a week, putting their initials in one circle for each kind act.

Learning Objective: To help children recognize that their advice can benefit others

Skill: Social communication

Ask the group, "What does it mean to give advice?" Let them brainstorm answers.

Tell them:

> *Giving advice means trying to help another person with a solution that you think can solve a problem. Advice may also be called for when you think someone is going to do something wrong, or make a mistake, and you want to help them avoid doing it.*

Ask the children to pretend someone is asking them the following questions. Tell them to remember that advice should help make a situation better or easier. What would their advice be?

- What should I do about not finishing my homework?

- What should I do if my mom is angry with me?

- What should I do if I'm not picked for the team?

After they have given advice for these questions, have them think of their own question-and-advice scenarios.

Learning Objective: To teach children to accept advice from others

Skill: Social communication

Ask the group for examples of when they got good advice and how they acted when they heard the advice.

Tell them:

> Sometimes people have trouble accepting advice because they think the person giving it is a "know-it-all." They may feel that they're being told what to do. They may also feel criticized, as though they can't decide for themselves. Most of the time, however, people give advice to help others. The person who is being advised can choose to accept the advice or not.

Distribute Activity Sheet 54 and have the children put a check next to the answers they think appropriate. Discuss their answers, and have them explain their choices.

Name ——————————————— **Date** ———————————

Put a check next to the best way to respond to the advice given below.

Advice: "I think you should tell the teacher she's wrong."

_____ "You're right. That's what I'll do."

_____ "Thanks for your advice." (and then walk away)

_____ "That doesn't sound like good advice to me."

Advice: "You should probably start studying for the math test a few days early."

_____ "I'm too busy to study."

_____ "That sounds like good advice."

_____ "I don't need to study—I already know everything."

Advice: "I think it's a good idea to get in shape before basketball season starts."

_____ "I'm in good shape already."

_____ "That's probably good advice."

_____ "What's the point? I won't make the team anyway."

Advice: "You should wear a helmet when you ride your bike."

_____ "It doesn't look cool."

_____ "I know. It's the safe thing to do."

_____ "Sam doesn't wear his, so why should I wear mine?"

Learning Objective: To teach children the meaning of positive friendships

Skill: Making friends

Ask the children, "What does it mean to be a friend to someone?" Have them brainstorm ideas as you write them on the blackboard or a large sheet of paper.

Tell them:

> You can make a friend by being a friend to another person. Friendships come in all forms, but it is always important to make friends who will bring out the best in you and who will be there for you when you need them. People you choose as your friends will usually have some of the same interests you do.
>
> Here are some things kids have said are important to them when they make a friend:
>
> • Treat your friends the way you want to be treated.
>
> • When your friend is talking to you, always pay attention.
>
> • If your friend tells you a secret, keep it. Don't tell anyone.
>
> • Always share things with your friend.
>
> • Always tell your friend the truth.
>
> • Always stick up for your friend.
>
> • Take turns with your friend.

Distribute Activity Sheet 55. When the children have completed the sheet, have them share what they like about the friend they have chosen.

Name ——————————————————— Date ———————————

In the space below, draw one of your friends. Then list three things you really like about that friend.

Three things I really like about my friend are:

1. _____

2. _____

3. _____

Borrowing

Learning Objective: To teach children the appropriate way to borrow something, with respect for the other person's property

Skill: Respect

Ask the group what it means to borrow something. Ask them to talk about the importance of both getting a person's consent before borrowing something and returning it in the same condition. Brainstorm ideas and write them on the blackboard or a large sheet of paper.

Tell them:

> *Whenever someone has something that you would like to borrow, you always have to ask whether it is okay to borrow it. The person must first give you permission to use her possession. Most people will be happy to lend you something if they are confident that it will come back to them the same way it was given to you. By returning it in the same condition, you show the person that you respect her and her property.*

Ask the children to talk about how they would feel in the following scenarios:

- Your friend borrows a hair ribbon and loses it. She gives you another one, but it's not the same kind.

- You ask your brother if you can borrow his favorite sweatshirt, and he says no.

- Your teacher lends you a book, and you lose it.

- You borrow your friend's bike. When you return it, the tire is flat, but you're sure it's not your fault.

- Your friend offers to lend you her gloves, but you're afraid you might lose them.

Have the group think of other borrowing/lending scenarios to discuss.

Learning Objective: To teach children to respect the thoughts and feelings of others

Skill: Respect

Ask the children, "What does the word 'respect' mean?" Encourage them to give examples.

Tell the group:

> *Respecting others means listening to what they have to say and understanding that their opinions, likes and dislikes might be different from yours—and that's okay.*
>
> *It also means allowing them to express themselves without putting them down and letting them do what they want to do or what they feel is right without trying to persuade them otherwise (as long as it doesn't hurt anyone). You should always treat people the way you want them to treat you.*

Lead a discussion on respectful acts children see at school and at home, such as listening to a teacher or parent. Also talk about disrespectful acts, such as putting people down, ignoring them, bullying, and so on.

Learning Objective: To teach children to recognize opportunities to help others

Skill: Helpfulness

Ask the group, "How do you help other people?" As they give examples, write them on the blackboard or a large sheet of paper.

Tell them:

> *Offering help not only makes the other person feel good, but you also get satisfaction from knowing you have helped. The process involves several steps, including:*
>
> - *Deciding whether someone needs or wants your help*
> - *Thinking of what you could do to help*
> - *Asking whether you can help*
> - *Choosing the best time to help*
> - *Offering help*
> - *Helping*
>
> *Offering help can also mean volunteering to help others through charity work or service learning. Either way, helping others makes you feel good about yourself.*

Distribute Activity Sheet 58. After students give their answers, have them actually tell what they would say if they were in the situation (e.g., "Mom, what can I do to help you make dinner?").

Name ——————————————— **Date** ———————

How can this boy help his mother?
He can:

_____

_____

_____

How can one girl help the other girl? She
can:

_____

_____

_____

How can the grownup help this boy?
He can:

_____

_____

_____

How can this student help his teacher? He
can:

_____

_____

_____

Learning Objective: To teach children that it's okay to ask for help from and depend on others when necessary

Skill: Social communication

Ask the group, "What does it mean to depend on other people?" Brainstorm ideas and write them on the blackboard or a large sheet of paper.

Tell them:

There are many things you can do on your own, but some require the cooperation, help and special talents of others. When you work with others to achieve a goal, you build trust and friendship.

When you ask for help and depend on someone else, the other person feels needed and that you care about him.

Distribute Activity Sheet 59. Ask for volunteers to talk about whom they would depend on for several of the examples and tell why they chose that person.

Name ——————————————— **Date** ———————————

If you needed help with each of the tasks below, who would you depend on? Why did you choose that person?

Learning how to ride a bike ————————————————

————————————————————————————————

Getting better at a sport ——————————————————

————————————————————————————————

Learning a new idea ————————————————————

————————————————————————————————

Shoveling snow —————————————————————

————————————————————————————————

Shopping for clothes ———————————————————

————————————————————————————————

Doing your homework ———————————————————

————————————————————————————————

Deciding what to wear to a party ——————————————

————————————————————————————————

Problem Solving

Too often, we do not give children full credit for their capacity to solve problems. We frequently jump in to help them before they really need help. But more than 40 years of research has shown that, given opportunity and encouragement, children as young as five are capable of looking at different sides of an issue and solving both simple and complex interpersonal problems.

Skill in social situations has relatively little to do with a child's intellectual development. It develops from experience in social problem solving and adult encouragement toward self-reliance. The activities in this section are designed to give children experience in finding alternative solutions, evaluating solutions, thinking before they act, and evaluating their choices—cognitively-based skills that can all be learned with practice.

These activities can be supplemented by real-life experiences that ask children to participate in solving interpersonal problems, such as:

- **Family Meetings:** These meeting are most helpful when they are held weekly and involve a broad scope of discussions, not just behavioral issues or planning for activities.

- **Classroom Meetings:** These meetings should be held every day, and children should be encouraged to talk about current issues in the classroom, school, and community.

- **Peer Mediation:** This formal training teaches children how to act as facilitators, helping others negotiate their differences.

- **Playground Training:** With adult supervision, children can role-play common problems that occur in unstructured settings, such as the playground, school bus, or cafeteria. The staff that supervises children in these settings can also be trained to help children learn to solve their own problems.

Learning Objective: To teach children to recognize problem-causing behaviors

Skill: Social problem solving

Ask the group, "What are some ways other people behave that bother you?" List their responses on the blackboard or a large sheet of paper. This discussion should focus on behaviors that are disturbing, rather than naming, or blaming, the people who exhibit them.

Tell them:

It's normal to have problems with how others behave sometimes. We all see things differently, and two people looking at the same behavior may have very different reactions to it. That's true of other people's behavior as well as our own. The way we behave can cause problems, or it can help us get along with others.

Distribute Activity Sheet 60. After the children have completed it, ask for volunteers to share their pictures and explain what is happening. Write down the categories of problems that the children talk about, such as:

- Doing Chores
- Family Rules
- School Rules
- Schoolwork
- Sharing
- Arguing With Parents
- Problems With Friends

If a child describes a problem in a category that is already listed, put a check mark next to that category. Point out any categories that are talked about repeatedly.

Name _____ **Date** _____

On the top half of this page, draw a picture of something you do that might be a problem for others. On the bottom half, draw a picture of another person doing something that causes a problem for you.

I may cause a problem by:

Other people cause a problem for me when they:

Learning Objective: To teach children to focus their thinking on solving a problem rather than on blaming other people for the problem

Skill: Social problem solving, positive thinking

Ask the group, "On a scale of 1 to 10, with 1 equaling no problems and 10 equaling many problems, where do you rate yourself?" Ask the "ones" to raise their hands, then the "twos," and so on.

Tell them:

> There are people who feel that they have a lot of problems and people who feel that they don't have many serious problems at all. How people see themselves depends a lot on their attitude. Of course, some people really do have serious problems, like health issues, or family problems, or learning problems. But even with serious problems, a positive attitude makes finding a solution much easier. Everyone can learn to have a more positive, solution-focused attitude about their problems. It helps if you don't feel sorry for yourself and you don't blame others.

Read this example to the group:

Complaint: "Cleaning up my room is a pain. I'd much rather be out playing."

Positive statement: "I can get my room cleaned quickly. Maybe I'll even find the book I lost!"

Then, ask for volunteers to turn these complaints into more positive statements.

- I'm really terrible at baseball.
- No one ever invites me to come over.
- I hate the way my hair looks.
- Everyone is going to have a better summer vacation than me.
- I'm the shortest kid in the class.

Have the group suggest additional complaints that they can turn into positive statements.

Brainstorming

Learning Objective: To teach children the technique of brainstorming as a way of identifying several solutions to a problem

Skill: Social problem solving

Ask the group, "What is brainstorming?"

Tell them:

There is often more than one solution to a problem. It's not always easy to think of other solutions, and brainstorming can help. Brainstorming means saying anything that comes into your mind, without being concerned about how others will react. It's a great way for a group of people to come up with good solutions. Brainstorming usually doesn't take very long—about five minutes—and it can be really fun. It's designed to help you break out of your normal thinking patterns and find new ways of looking at things.

There are no limits in brainstorming—any idea is a good one at first. Everyone should try to come up with as many ideas as possible, and no one is permitted to judge or discuss these ideas. The solutions can be unusual, and they don't even have to make sense. No idea is too wacky or ridiculous. As crazy as any idea might seem, it might make someone think of another idea or a better idea. It might even turn out to be the best idea of all!

Give the group a problem and have them brainstorm as many ideas as possible. Write their ideas on the blackboard or a large sheet of paper. If time allows, evaluate and eliminate each solution until you come up with one on which everyone can agree.

Learning Objective: To reinforce the concept that there can be many solutions to the same problem

Skill: Social problem solving

Tell the children:

When you have a problem, it's a good idea to think of several ways to solve it. Your first solution may not be perfect, or it may not even work. If you have several possible solutions that seem good, you can try the one that seems best and sees if it works. You may even find that another would be better.

Distribute Activity Sheet 63. When the children have completed it, have them share their alternative solutions.

Name _____ Date _____

Can you think of three solutions to each of these problems? Then, think of a problem you need to solve. What are three ways you could solve it?

SOLUTION A	SOLUTION B
_____	_____

Katya, Fred, and Jacob all want to sit at the same desk.

SOLUTION C
_____

SOLUTION A	SOLUTION B
_____	_____

Bobby forgets to bring his project to school.

SOLUTION C
_____

SOLUTION A
_____

SOLUTION B
_____

A problem I need to solve is:
_____
_____

SOLUTION C
_____

Learning Objective: To help children decide on the best solution to a problem

Skill: Social problem solving

Ask the group why it is important to have more than one solution to a problem. If they have completed the previous activity, they should be familiar with this concept.

Tell them:

> *It's always best to have two or three solutions to a problem, but in the end you have to choose the one you think will work best. If you think of one solution at a time, and then think about what might happen if you chose that solution, you can come up with the best one. Of course, you can't know exactly what will happen until you try a solution, but thinking about it and planning can help.*

Have the children sit in a circle and count off by twos. If there is an odd number of children, the last child can be "1" and you can be "2." Read the first problem from the list below. The first "1" should give a possible solution, and the first "2" should give an alternative solution. Then ask the group to discuss which solution is better, and vote on it. Proceed with the next pair offering solutions to the second problem. You can continue this activity by asking children to suggest additional social problems they commonly encounter.

1. Kevin called Gloria "fat and ugly." What should she do?
2. Sarah didn't receive an invitation to her best friend's birthday party. What should she do?
3. Teresa wanted to invite Shannon over to play, but she was afraid Shannon wouldn't come. What should she do?
4. Brian was always chosen last when it was time to pick a sports team. What should he do?
5. Seth was new at school and didn't know how to make friends. What should he do?

Learning Objective: To teach children how to evaluate the outcome of a solution and to react appropriately when they make mistakes

Skill: Social problem solving

Tell the children:

We've already practiced thinking of different solutions to a problem and choosing the one you thought would work best. Now, we're going to think about what to do when a solution doesn't work. You may do something that seems right at the time, but doesn't get the results you want. Or, you may do something that just makes things worse. The important thing to remember is not to be upset or embarrassed if you make a mistake. Just try to think about what went wrong, and what you can do next. Everyone makes mistakes and hopefully you learn from your mistakes and don't repeat them.

Ask the group what they would suggest to the children in these examples:

1. Teresa thought that her big brother was mean to her. She told her mother, who punished her brother. But then he was even meaner! What should Teresa do?

2. Frank wanted to be friends with Nate, so he gave him one of his best trading cards. But Nate still didn't want to play with him. What should Frank do?

3. Erin wanted to get her ears pierced. She gave her mom a drawing she had made, thinking that her mother would be so pleased that she would let Erin get her ears pierced. But Erin's mother still said, "Sorry, but you can't have pierced ears until you are 16." What would you tell Erin to do?

4. Sean was not a good reader and he was embarrassed to read in front of the class. He asked his father to write a note to his teacher, saying that Sean had a sore throat and couldn't read out loud. But his father wouldn't write the note. What would you tell Sean to do?

Learning Objective: To teach children the importance of thinking in advance about the reasons for, and consequences of, their actions

Skill: Decision-making, self-control

Ask the group, "Why is it important to think before you act?" Brainstorm reasons and write them on the blackboard or a large sheet of paper.

Tell them:

Thinking before acting involves self-control, and it can help you solve problems. Before you react impulsively or in anger, gather the facts in your mind, think about them, and then act appropriately. It will take you only seconds—your mind is constantly processing these thoughts as you go about your business.

If you ran into the street to chase a ball without first gathering information about your actions, you all know what could happen. And when you know what might happen, you can avoid making wrong decisions or feeling bad about your actions.

Distribute Activity Sheet 66. When children have offered their answers, lead a discussion about the consequences of acting without thinking.

Name ——————————————————— Date ———————————

Answer these questions any way you would like, keeping "thinking before acting" in mind.

Brian stole my lunch!

Emily

How does Emily know this? _____

Does it sound like Emily is accusing Brian? _____

Why would Emily think Brian did it? _____

Do you think Emily thought before she spoke? _____

Paolo hit me!

How does Owen know Paolo hit him? _____

Did he actually see Paolo hit him? _____

Why would he think Paolo did it? _____

What would be the best thing for Owen to do? _____

Learning Objective: To help children learn the consequences of misbehavior; to decide if an action is worth taking

Skill: Decision-making, social problem solving

Tell the group:

Before you do something you think might be wrong, you should consider what might happen—who might be hurt, what might be damaged, and so on. Rules are made for a purpose, and it's always smart to make good choices. Good choices can help you solve problems and avoid creating new problems. But if you decide to make an unwise choice, you should be ready to accept the consequences. You may think you can get away with it, but ultimately someone or something will be harmed.

Distribute Activity Sheet 67. When the children have completed it, have them talk about why they think they chose wisely and what consequences the other options might have.

Name _____ Date _____

In each situation, put a check next to the choice(s) you think would be wise. If none of the choices seem quite right, write your own, but be sure it's a wise choice.

Your teacher asks you to put the chairs on the desks after school. You:

_____ Get someone to help you put the chairs on the desks.

_____ Say, "Okay," and then forget to do it.

_____ Clean the blackboard and erasers instead.

_____ _____

Your mom tells you to clean your room. You:

_____ Pay your little sister to clean it.

_____ Clean it.

_____ Promise to do it after school.

_____ _____

You see some kids take another kid's book bag and run away. You:

_____ Don't do anything.

_____ Run after the kids and try to get it back.

_____ Tell the kid to stand up for himself.

_____ _____

You find a wallet on the playground. You:

_____ Take the money and leave the wallet.

_____ Take the wallet home and hide it.

_____ Take the wallet to the school office and hand it in.

_____ _____

Learning Objective: To help children accept the consequences of their behavior and make changes when necessary

Skill: Social problem solving, conflict resolution

Explain to the group:

A consequence is something that naturally follows from an action or behavior. If you don't do your homework, you won't get credit for it and you may be in trouble. If you are mean to a friend, he will be mad at you and may not want to be your friend. These events are the consequences of your behavior. Understanding that all your behaviors have consequences will help you solve—and even avoid—problems in your relationships with others.

Because two people may see the same event differently, you may think that a consequence is unfair, or that you didn't even do anything wrong. Taking the time to think and talk about what happened will help you and the other person work things out. If someone thinks you did something wrong, here's what you can do:

- *Decide whether what you did was really wrong.*
- *If it was, admit it was wrong.*
- *Try to explain why you did it. (You may not really know why, but thinking about it can help you find out.)*
- *Accept the consequences without complaining. That might help you never do the same thing again!*

Ask the group to talk about personal experiences when they had to deal with consequences of their behavior. Did they think the consequences were fair? Why or why not? Then, have them think of scenarios involving wrongdoing and decide on appropriate consequences. Some examples are: being late to class, cutting in line, and cheating on a test.

Group Problem Solving*

Learning Objective: To teach children to solve problems in a group situation

Skill: Social problem solving

Ask the group, "Why is it important to learn to solve problems as a group?" Write their reasons on the blackboard or a large sheet of paper.

Tell them:

> *Group problem solving is a process for helping people work together. It is guided by two main rules: the discussion is always directed toward solving the problem, and it never centers around whose fault the problem is.*

> *The group works to understand and respect different points of view, focus on the problem, communicate everyone's wants and feelings, and cooperate to solve the problem. The solution can incorporate good ideas from each person in the group.*

Distribute Activity Sheet 69. Talk about how important it is to listen, speak in turn, never criticize, and so on, and also about how much compromising is required in group problem solving.

Have the group sit in a circle, and choose one person to read the rules. Then have someone else choose one of the problems on the sheet, or ask the group to suggest different problems. After each problem is discussed, ask for someone to summarize what has been said. In accordance with the rules, the group should try to come up with a solution that satisfies everyone.

Rules

- Everyone is responsible for listening to the speaker.

- Everyone must share his or her point of view about the problem.

- No one is allowed to interrupt the speaker.

- Everyone will show respect for others. No one can make fun of or criticize anyone else's ideas.

Problems

- The group must choose a place to go for a class trip.

- The group must choose a gift for someone.

- There aren't enough seats for everyone at the school play.

- There are ten people and only six pieces of cake.

- Two teams want to practice basketball but there is only one ball.

Listening: A Two-Way Street

Listening skills are much more complex than most people realize, involving both an intellectual and an emotional give-and-take. These skills are essential for effective social communication, which is like a dance that requires both participants to be in step.

Many children are so focused on making their own points in a conversation that they don't take the time to consider the thoughts, feelings, and needs of others. When children dominate conversations with their peers, they are frequently seen as bossy, selfish, or aggressive.

Adults, naturally, are concerned when children are poor listeners. They expect children age five and up to be able to comprehend what they are saying and to respond or behave appropriately. Unfortunately, more often than not, children do not meet this expectation. Many children today don't seem to listen and respond appropriately to adults, and they typically begin to be characterized as willful or oppositional. If these problems persist, serious behavioral problems may follow.

There is no question that the ability to listen and respond appropriately is part of some children's innate temperament. But there is also strong evidence that children who do not have this ability innately can be taught the skill. Certainly, helping children learn and practice listening skills is a much more effective approach to improving behavior than reprimands and punishment.

In teaching children listening skills as part of a social skills program, it is also important to consider whether or not their problems in listening may be due to a learning disability or other undetected problem. Hearing screenings are typically done by schools as well as by pediatricians, and although not the typical reason why children are poor social listeners, hearing difficulties would be the first cause to rule out. Learning difficulties, including auditory processing and information processing problems, should also be ruled out. Finally, a diagnostician should consider whether there is a nonverbal learning disability that may be contributing to a child's listening problems. Although there is no standardized test to evaluate this problem, a protocol for determining if a nonverbal learning disability is part of the problem can be found in a book by Stephen Nowicki and Marshall Duke, entitled *Helping the Child Who Doesn't Fit In* (Peachtree Publishers, 1992).

Learning Objective: To teach children the difference between just hearing and actually listening

Skill: Emotional communication, social awareness

Ask the group to share their ideas on the difference between hearing and listening. Then, tell them:

> There's a big difference between hearing and listening. You can hear a train coming and you can hear a dog barking. You can also hear a person speaking. But when that person is speaking, are you really listening? You may just be hearing her words; if you are also listening to her, you are both hearing and understanding her words.

Ask the group to suggest times when it's important to really listen instead of just hearing, such as:

• when a teacher is explaining homework

• when a friend is feeling sad and sharing his feelings

• when your mom is telling you how to cook something

After volunteers have shared their ideas, have them think of times when just hearing something is sufficient. For example, people can hear music or the wind blowing in the trees, without really thinking about what they are hearing. Then, ask them what would happen if people didn't really listen to each other.

Learning Objective: To teach children to take turns talking and listening during a conversation

Skill: Social communication, self-control

Ask the group why it is important to listen when they are having a conversation with someone. Brainstorm ideas and write them on the blackboard or a large sheet of paper.

Tell them:

> *When you listen carefully while others speak, people feel that you are interested in what they have to say. You may want to make a point, but it is important to use self-control and listen to the other person.*
>
> *Here are some important rules to follow:*
>
> - *You should show interest in what the person is saying by facing her and maintaining eye contact.*
>
> - *While she is speaking, think about what she's saying to you.*
>
> - *If you agree with what she's saying, or want to show that you understand, you can nod your head.*
>
> - *When she's finished speaking, ask a question or make a comment about what she said.*
>
> *People want to feel that they are being heard and understood. When you are a good listener, people will see you as a caring, respectful person and they will connect with you more easily.*

Distribute Activity Sheet 71. After the children complete it, ask them why they think certain pairs of kids are going to have a good conversation and others are not. For the pairs that are not, have the group suggest responses that good listeners might make. Then, have children pair up and try to have conversations themselves, either independently or by bringing one pair to the front of the class at a time.

Name _____ Date _____

Some of these children are really listening to their partners, and others are not. Circle the pairs that are on their way to having a good conversation.

Learning Objective: To teach children to learn information by listening attentively

Skill: Social communication, social awareness

Ask the group why it is important to listen for information when someone is speaking.

Tell them:

> *When someone is telling you something, it's important to listen carefully, especially if he is giving you new information about something you have to do, somewhere you have to go, and so on. If your teacher is teaching a lesson, you can't learn it if you're not listening and understanding.*

Have one child begin a story, for example, by saying, "Once there was a dog that got on a city bus..." In turn, each child adds another sentence until the story is finished. The children must listen to the entire story as it progresses, and their contributions must be relevant to the information that came before. Children can then write or recite a short summary about what happened in the story.

Another alternative is to have each child think of an object and give four clues about it. After the other children in the group have listened to all four clues, they can try to guess what the object is.

Have the children discuss whether it is easy or difficult to listen carefully when they have to find out information about something new.

Learning Objective: To teach children the importance of following instructions

Skill: Social communication, respect

Ask the group, "Why is it important to follow instructions? What would happen if people didn't follow instructions?" Brainstorm ideas and write them on the blackboard or a large sheet of paper.

Tell them:

> When you follow instructions, life goes more smoothly. If everyone in this group did only what they wanted to, it would be hard for us to accomplish our goals. There would probably be arguments and hurt feelings. When one person doesn't listen, the whole group can be affected. When everyone works to complete tasks together, there are usually good feelings in the group.
>
> There are five main steps to following instructions. First, make sure you look at the speaker. Second, listen carefully, and third, think about what the speaker is saying. Fourth, ask questions if you need to. Finally, follow the instructions.

Distribute Activity Sheet 73. Have the children cut out the parts of the two sets of instructions. Then read the following lists of instructions to them—one at a time and several times if necessary—so that they can complete the activity correctly:

1. Take out your science book.	1. Get out of bed.
2. Turn to page 23.	2. Wash your face.
3. Open your notebook.	3. Brush your teeth.
4. Take out a pencil.	4. Brush your hair.
5. Answer questions 1–15.	5. Get dressed.
6. Put your books away.	6. Eat breakfast.

When they have completed the activity sheet, talk about whether it was easy or difficult to follow the instructions.

Make a copy of this page for each child. Have them cut out the pieces and turn them over so that they can't see what is written on each piece. After you have read each list of instructions, have them turn the pieces over and put them in the right order.

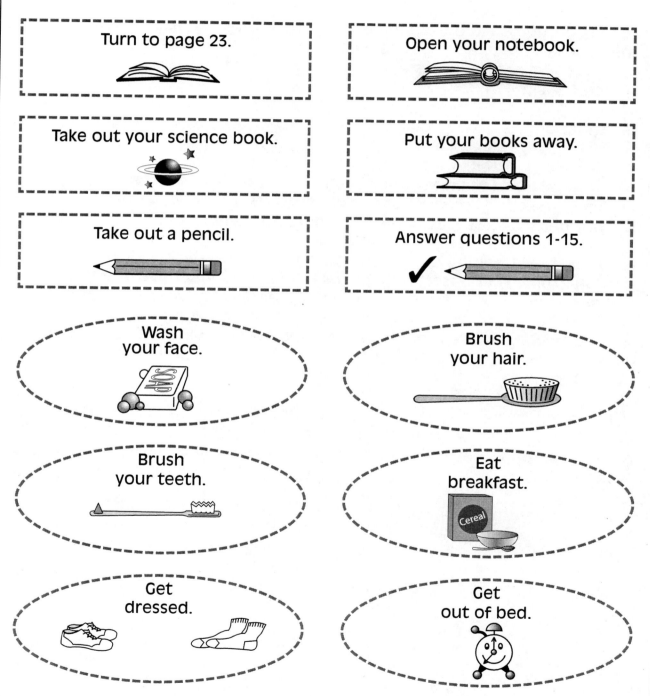

Turn to page 23.

Open your notebook.

Take out your science book.

Put your books away.

Take out a pencil.

Answer questions 1-15.

Wash your face.

Brush your hair.

Brush your teeth.

Eat breakfast.

Get dressed.

Get out of bed.

Learning Objective: To teach children to listen with complete attention and reflect back what the other person has said

Skill: Social communication, social awareness

Ask the group, "What do you think 'reflective listening' means?" Suggest that they think of the two words separately, which may help them determine the meaning. Brainstorm ideas and write them on the blackboard or a large sheet of paper.

Tell the group:

Reflective listening is listening to someone with your complete attention and then repeating what she has said in your own words. If your reflection is correct, she might say, "Yes, that's what I said." If it's not quite right, she may say, "No, that's not what I said."

Reflective listening is often used when the speaker is talking about something that upsets her. If your friend said, "I feel so sad because my cat died," you might say, "You're upset because your cat died. It's hard for you to deal with," instead of, "You can always get another cat." Reflective listening shows that you have empathy for the other person—you understand how she is feeling, and she feels that you are supporting her.

Pair the children and have them talk about any of the subjects below. After two minutes, one speaker restates what the other one has said, using reflective, empathetic language. Then the speakers switch, choosing another topic.

- Something that really bothers me is...

- At school, something that is really hard for me is...

- One problem I have at school is...

- Once, I was teased about...

Learning Objective: To teach children a method of listening that promotes sustained conversation

Skill: Social communication, social awareness

Ask the group, "What do you think 'active listening' means?" Tell them that thinking of the words separately may help them figure out the meaning. Brainstorm ideas and write them on the blackboard or a large sheet of paper.

Tell them:

In active listening, you are listening to what the person is saying and interpreting, or trying to get the meaning of, her message. Active listening can help keep a conversation going, and it can help you get to know someone better. You should never bring up your own experiences—active listening is only about what the other person is saying. There are four main steps in active listening:

1. **Attending:** *Attending means hearing and understanding. The person can tell you're listening because of your body language— your face shows interest and you're making appropriate eye contact and gestures, such as nodding encouragingly.*

2. **Paraphrasing:** *After you have listened to the person, you paraphrase, or say in your own words, what you have heard. For example, if the person told you he was angry about forgetting his book, you might say, "You feel angry because you forgot to bring your book home."*

3. **Clarifying:** *Clarifying means asking for more information to make sure you understand. You could ask: "Can you tell me more about...?" or "How do you feel about it?"*

4. **Feedback:** *Giving feedback involves describing what you understand about the person's feelings. Using the earlier example, you could say, "Forgetting your book made you worry that you would get in trouble. You feel like you weren't being responsible."*

Hand out Activity Sheet 75 and divide the group into pairs. When the activity is completed, lead a discussion on the benefits of active listening.

With your partner, take turns being the speaker and the listener:

1. The speaker reads the statement.
2. The listener restates it in his own words and asks questions, such as those below, to clarify.
3. When the speaker has answered, the listener should describe his understanding of the speaker's feelings.

Speaker: I was in line in the cafeteria, and a bunch of kids cut in front of me.

Listener: A bunch of kids cut in front of you in the cafeteria.
- Can you tell me more about it?
- What happened next?
- How do you feel about it?

Speaker: I didn't clean my room, so my mom took my CD player away.

Listener: Your mom took your CD player because you didn't clean your room.
- Can you tell me more about it?
- What happened next?
- How do you feel about it?

Speaker: My locker door was stuck, and I was late for class.

Listener: You were late for class because your locker door was stuck.
- Can you tell me more about it?
- What happened next?
- How do you feel about it?

Learning Objective: To teach children how to give positive feedback

Skill: Social communication, making friends

Ask the group, "What is positive feedback?" Tell them to think of the two words separately, which may help them determine the meaning. Brainstorm ideas and write them on the blackboard or a large sheet of paper.

Tell them:

Being a good listener doesn't mean you just listen without commenting on what's being said. When you give positive feedback, you have the opportunity to reinforce what's been said. You can also compliment the speaker on his insight or ideas and say anything positive that reflects your agreement and support.

Positive feedback is the opposite of criticism. It is always welcome. It shows that you have been listening, it encourages the speaker to continue, and it shows that you care about him. Even if the person is saying something negative, with positive feedback you can change a negative exchange into a positive one. When you give someone positive feedback, you feel good too.

Distribute Activity Sheet 76. After the children complete it, have them share and discuss their positive feedback statements.

Name _____ Date _____

I got a new CD player.

That's cool. What kind is it?

What positive response could you give to each statement below?

"I never get anything new."

_____

"I don't think I can do the social studies homework."

_____

"My mom is making a special dinner tonight."

_____

"I have to visit relatives on Saturday night and can't go to the party."

_____

Then, write your own statements and responses below:

Statement _____

Response _____

Standing Up For Yourself

Many children with social skill problems have difficulty asserting their rights in appropriate ways. Shy children are vulnerable to being teased or bullied. Aggressive children may not realize that they can fulfill their needs and wants in ways that take into account the needs and wants of others. And all children—even those with adequate social skills—are subject to peer pressure, which can put them at risk for drug and alcohol use and sexual experimentation.

The ability to be assertive in positive and respectful ways is a skill that will have tremendous developmental significance for every child. At every stage of life, we are faced with situations that require us to be assertive. Our ability to handle those situations effectively can literally shape the course of our lives.

A sense of personal power and the ability to have a positive attitude even when facing problems are essential building blocks of assertiveness, which requires different skills in different situations. Standing up for themselves also means that children have to differentiate assertiveness from aggressiveness. They must learn that they have certain rights that should not be violated, and that they must also respect and even protect the rights of others.

Handling bullying and teasing requires a special set of skills, because it involves dealing with children who are typically very aggressive and have been successful in victimizing others. Many schools today have anti-bullying and drug prevention programs that teach positive self-assertion. If the activities in this section reflect the goals of these programs, they may be expanded to broader usage in the school.

Learning Objective: To teach children the benefits of having a positive self-concept

Skill: Self-awareness

Ask the group, "Who feels good about him- or herself?" As children raise their hands, ask them what makes them feel good about themselves. Write their reasons on the blackboard or a large sheet of paper.

Tell them:

> *Having a positive attitude—feeling good about yourself, the things you do, the way you do them, and the important things and people in your life—can make you feel confident and secure. It will help you in school and in dealing with others. A positive attitude will help you throughout your life.*

Have the children think of recent experiences that made them feel good. List these experiences on a blackboard or a large sheet of paper. They might include: a trip, a favorite activity, time with friends, time with family, and so on. Ask the group to talk about which experiences had the biggest impact on how they felt about themselves, and why.

Learning Objective: To teach children that their behavior affects their attitude

Skill: Positive thinking, self-awareness

Ask the group, "Think of some things you did this week that you consider to be positive. How did these things make you feel?"

Tell them:

Some people naturally have a positive outlook on life. Other people seem to have a negative outlook on life. If you have a negative outlook and only see the problems or the disappointments in your life, you can learn to have a more positive attitude. You can learn to focus on your good qualities, and not your problems. You can learn to think about things you want to improve in your life and then work to make them better. When you do, you will feel better about yourself. Other people will probably feel better about you, too.

Distribute Activity Sheet 78. Have the children share one thing they've written from each column and explain why they think they do that thing well or why they would like to do it better.

Name _____ **Date** _____

In the left column, write or draw three things you'd like change about yourself or do better at. In the right column, write or draw what you can do to have a more positive attitude about these things.

I'm not a good soccer player.	I can practice soccer every day.

Learning Objective: To teach children the importance of sticking up for themselves

Skill: Assertiveness

Ask the group, "What does 'sticking up for yourself' mean?" Ask them for examples.

Tell them:

Sometimes children are shy and don't say what they want or need. But sticking up for yourself—saying what you want or need—can be an important step toward getting it.

There are many reasons why some children don't stick up for themselves. They may feel embarrassed about calling attention to themselves. They may feel that if they stick up for themselves, other children will get angry or even pick on them. Some children may not feel that their needs or feelings are very important. But everyone is important. Everyone deserves to be heard. Everyone deserves to try to get what they need to be happy.

Ask the group how the children in the following situations could stick up for themselves:

- The other children never ask Marcia to join their games at recess, and she really wants to play.
- Reed's teacher never calls on him, even when his hand is in the air first.
- Dana wants to sit at the lunch table with her friend Grace. Caitlin, who is bossy, has told Dana to go sit somewhere else.
- Callie feels that her mother only pays attention to her baby sister.
- Jose is new at school, and no one ever talks to him or makes him feel welcome.

Learning Objective: To teach children the importance of giving themselves credit

Skill: Positive thinking

Tell the group to give themselves a pat on the back. Then, ask them what it symbolizes. Brainstorm ideas and write them on the blackboard or a large sheet of paper.

Continue:

> We all have inner critics that tell us things like, "You'll never get an A, no matter how hard you study," or "You'll always be fat." When a thought like this comes into your head, you can visualize a stop sign and turn your negative thought into a positive one: "I can try to get an A, but a B is okay too," or "I can try to lose weight, and if I stick to my diet, I will." Instead of just criticizing yourself, you can give yourself a pat on the back whenever you feel like you need one.
>
> It's a good feeling when another person recognizes something good that you did, but the important thing is for you to give yourself credit for what you've done. So, if you do something good and nobody notices, you can still pat yourself on the back. You don't need the recognition of others to feel good about yourself.

Distribute Activity Sheet 80. Have the children discuss what they did and why they can feel good about it, even if no one else realizes what they've done.

Name_____ **Date**_____

I, _____, did something really great.

I (*write what you did*)_____

_____

_____.

It made me feel _____

_____.

(*write how it made you feel*)

Congratulations to me!

Learning Objective: To teach children alternatives for responding to physical aggression

Skill: Conflict resolution

Ask the group, "If someone hit or kicked you, what would you do?"

Tell them:

Physical violence is never the answer to being hit, shoved, or otherwise assaulted. If someone hits you, your initial reaction will probably be anger. You may want to hit back, but it will just make things worse. Instead, you should try to talk to the person who hit you, or walk away and tell an adult. Fighting never solves the problem.

Lead a discussion about the realities of avoiding fights. Ask group members what they would do in these situations:

- A child from another team intentionally tripped you while playing ball.
- An older child took your lunch and pushed you down.
- Another child wanted your lunch money. He twisted your arm to make you give it to him.
- You got shoved in the lunch line, and your tray fell on the floor.

Encourage the students to make up additional scenarios and discuss what they would do.

Learning Objective: To teach children how to avoid bullies and what to do if they become victims of bullying

Skill: Assertiveness

Ask the group, "What is a bully? Can you give me examples of what bullies do to other children?"

Explain that:

> A bully is a child who uses cruel behavior to make another child feel bad. Bullying may happen often, and it usually continues over time. It can include taunting, name-calling, threats, stealing, and fighting. Bullies may seem like they're stronger and more in control than other kids, but they are actually unsure of themselves. They act mean to get attention and power.
>
> It can be very hard to deal with bullies because they know how to make people afraid. Sometimes, they get other children to join in their bullying. To avoid being bullied, try your hardest to stay away from bullies. You can also be assertive and say something like, "I'm ignoring you. I don't like being bullied." You can walk away and tell an adult that you are being bullied. Your friends may help you, but bullies can be very frightening and other children may not want to get involved.

Ask children to talk about incidents of bullying they have seen at school. They may choose to talk about things that have happened to them, or they may feel more comfortable talking about incidents that have happened to others.

- What happened?
- Why do you think you (or the child) were chosen as the victim?
- How did you (or the other child) react?
- What could you (or the other child) have done differently?
- What would you do (or suggest doing) if this happens again?

Learning Objective: To teach children to deal with being teased

Skill: Assertiveness

Ask the group, "What is teasing, and why do people tease others?"

Tell them:

> Sometimes, people tease each other in a good-natured way. They may say something like, "Don't trip!"—after you've already fallen. This kind of teasing is a way that people try to be funny, although it often isn't very funny to the person being teased.
>
> When people are trying to hurt your feelings or make you angry, they are teasing in a mean way. Mean teasing includes name-calling, put-downs, and other forms of ridicule.
>
> It is usually easy for you to tell whether someone is teasing you to be mean or to be funny. In either case, if you don't like being teased, here are some things you can do to stop it:
>
> - Ignore it and don't give those teasing you the satisfaction of seeing you get upset.
> - Help yourself by visualizing their teasing "bouncing" off you, as if you had a shield protecting you.
> - Say "So?" to show the teasers that what they are saying doesn't matter to you.
> - Have a sense of humor and realize that no one is perfect.
>
> If you are being teased and feel like you need help, be sure to tell an adult.

Distribute Activity Sheet 83. When the children have completed the activity, lead a discussion on how it feels to be teased and what the best ways to respond are.

don't let what a bully say
I'm pretty cool
everyone likes you

Name _____ **Date** _____

Below each picture, write what you could say if someone teased you.

You're such a nerd!

I could say _____

_____

You're the teacher's pet!

I could say _____

_____

Now, fill in the speech balloons with words that have been used to tease you. How did you respond? Is there a better way you could have responded?

I said _____

I could have said _____

_____

I said _____

I could have said _____

_____

Learning Objective: To teach children to recognize stress and be able to reduce it

Skill: Coping

Ask the group, "Can anyone tell me what stress is? Has anyone ever felt 'stressed out'?"

Tell them:

> Stress is something that makes you feel uncomfortable. You probably feel stress when you have to take a test or when you are up at bat in a baseball game. These kinds of stress are normal. You also feel stress when you are teased, or when your parents argue at home, or when someone in your family is sick. These are more serious forms of stress, and it's important to learn to cope with them.
>
> Even if you can't change the circumstances that make you feel stressed, there are ways to deal with stress. You can:
>
> - Talk about what is bothering you.
> - Take deep breaths and relax.
> - Exercise—physical activity reduces stress.
> - Eat well and get plenty of sleep.
> - Think about the positive and fun things in your life.
> - Learn to solve problems in a positive way.

Ask everyone to think of one thing that causes stress in their lives. Then ask for volunteers to talk about their own stress and how they can cope with it better. If the speaker agrees, the rest of the group can offer suggestions on ways to deal with this stress.

Learning Objective: To teach children how to recognize pressure to conform to a group

Skill: Assertiveness

Ask the group if they ever feel like they have to do some things just because other children are doing them—for example, wearing certain clothes or watching certain TV shows because everyone else does. Have the children offer examples of times they've felt pressured to do certain things.

Tell them:

Group pressure is what you feel when other children try to influence you to do something. It can be good, or positive, pressure—for example, when your friends encourage you to try a new sport. It can also be negative, such as when your friends ask you to do something that you know is wrong, like breaking a school rule.

Everyone feels pressure to act a certain way or to do certain things. But how you act is your choice. You should never feel that you have to do something just because other children tell you it is the "cool" thing to do. You should make your choice by deciding if what they want you to do is good for you or not.

Distribute Activity Sheet 85. Ask children to decide whether or not they would follow the group in these situations. Then, discuss their answers.

Name _____ **Date** _____

Next to each situation, write "Y" if you would go along with the group and "N" if you would not.

_____ Your friends want you to eat at the same lunch table.

_____ Your friends want you to shoplift candy with them.

_____ Your friends ask you to play baseball with them.

_____ Your friends want you to join a secret club.

_____ Your friends want you to play a video game that you know your parents disapprove of.

_____ Your friends want you to go see an "R-rated" movie.

_____ Your friends ask if they can copy your homework.

_____ Your friends want you to hang out at the mall, and your parents don't like you doing this.

Write your own situations below:

_____ _____ .

_____ _____ .

Learning Objective: To teach children how to refuse when pressured by peers to do something they don't want to do

Skill: Assertiveness

Ask the group, "When do you think it is important to say no, even though other people want you to go along with them?" Have them provide examples.

Tell them:

It's often very hard to say no when others ask you to do something you don't want to do. It may seem easier to just go along with the group. But it's important to know that you always have a choice, and that you are free to make that choice—it's up to you.

If you say no, and the other kids ask why, be honest and tell them why you won't or can't do what they want you to do. Most of the time, people will respect you for your decisions. You should never feel guilty for saying no; you should be proud of being true to yourself.

Have the group practice saying no in different situations. Ask for a volunteer, who will try to convince the other children to give in. This volunteer has only 30 seconds with each participant and can exert pressure in any way, except by using bad language or by touching the other person. Then ask for another volunteer. After each round, discuss the different ways children can say no.

Here are some suggested situations. Children can also suggest their own.

- I want you to come and steal some candy with me.
- Let's tease David, and see if we can get him to cry.
- Try this cigarette; it's fun to smoke.
- Let's cut class. No one will catch us.
- Tell your parents you're sleeping at my house. We can sneak out and go to the mall.

Learning Objective: To teach children to release their anger in non-aggressive ways

Skill: Emotional control

Ask the group, "What are some ways people release their anger?" Brainstorm ideas and write them on the blackboard or a large sheet of paper.

Explain that:

Anger is a healthy and natural response to frustration. It's okay to feel angry, and it's not good for you to ignore or hide your anger. If you do that, you may start to feel sad, or even sick.

No one will ever know you're angry if you don't express your feelings, but it's important to release your anger without harming others or hurting their feelings. If you lose control, you might say or do things you'll regret later.

Here are some safe ways to release anger:

- *Talk to someone who cares about you and will listen.*
- *Draw a picture of what's making you angry or write about it.*
- *Hit a pillow.*
- *Exercise.*
- *Count to ten slowly.*
- *Breathe deeply.*

Distribute Activity Sheet 87. When completed, discuss the anger-inciting situations and ask volunteers to talk about the ones that make them angry. Discuss their suggestions for safe ways to release anger.

Name _____ **Date** _____

Put a check next to each situation that makes you angry. For the situations you've checked, tell how you can express your anger safely. On the blank line, add your own example.

1-2-3-4-5-6...

_____ When I ask for something and don't get it, I could:

_____

_____ When someone takes something of mine without asking first, I could:

_____

_____ When someone calls me a name, I could:

_____

_____ When someone tells me to do something I don't want to do, I could:

_____

_____ When my mom or dad scolds me, I could:

_____

_____ When someone blames me for something I didn't do, I could:

_____

_____ When something isn't fair, I could:

_____

_____ When someone bosses me around, I could:

_____

_____ When someone ignores me, I could:

_____

_____ When _____, I could: _____

_____

Learning Objective: To teach children that they have certain rights which can't be taken away and responsibilities that go along with these rights

Skill: Assertiveness, responsibility

Ask the group to give examples of rights and responsibilities. Write their responses on the blackboard or a large sheet of paper.

Tell them:

Rights are things that you should always expect to have. For example, you have the right to feel safe, the right to a place to live, the right to have enough to eat, and the right to an education. Along with these rights, you also have responsibilities. Here are some examples:

- *You have the right to feel safe, and you have the responsibility not to do things that may hurt you or others.*
- *You have the right to have a place to live, and you have the responsibility to keep your room clean and to help around the house.*
- *You have the right to have enough to eat, and you have the responsibility to yourself to eat things that are good for you.*
- *You have the right to an education, and you have the responsibility to use the opportunity wisely and work hard in school.*

Everyone can learn to be more responsible by:
- *Using their own resources and judgment to make decisions*
- *Acting independently*
- *Considering the effect of their actions on others*
- *Meeting their own needs without disregarding the needs of others*
- *Finding positive solutions to their problems*

Ask the children to give specific examples of some of their responsibilities and to tell how fulfilling these responsibilities affects them or others. Examples could be: I pick up trash when I see it, so I'll have a cleaner community, or I wash my hands before I eat, so I won't get sick.

Learning Objective: To teach children how to assert their own rights without infringing on the rights of others

Skill: Assertiveness

Explain to the children that there is a difference between being assertive and being aggressive.

Tell them:

You have many different rights, including the right to be safe, and the right to have the things you own left alone. If someone threatens you, teases you, or takes something that belongs to you, they are taking away your rights and being aggressive.

Being assertive means sticking up for your rights or the rights of others. It does not mean taking away the rights of others. For example, if a child grabbed your book and you reacted by pushing him, you would both be aggressive. If you clearly and firmly told him to return your book, you would be assertive.

It is important to be assertive, sticking up for yourself and also for other children, particularly if they are younger or smaller. It is not always easy, and it may mean speaking up when you are afraid. Even if you feel like you are tattling, you may need to get an adult to help you.

Ask the group to share examples of assertiveness from their own behavior or from their observations. Then, copy Activity Sheet 89 and cut out the cards. Turn them facedown and pick any card. Choosing an Assertor and an Aggressor, ask two children to role-play the situation described. Next, pick two other children to role-play the next card. Make sure that children have a chance to be both Assertor and Aggressor.

Aggressor: You are a bully trying to get the other person's snack.

Assertor: You try to stop the bully without being rude or angry.

Aggressor: You say something mean about the other child's family.

Assertor: You respond calmly and firmly, saying how you feel without getting angry.

Aggressor: You call the other child "stupid," because he is having trouble in school.

Assertor: You say how name-calling makes you feel without getting into an argument.

Aggressor: You tell the other child s/he isn't good enough to join the dodge ball game.

Assertor: You say that you have a right to play just like anyone else and find a

---

Aggressor: You make faces to annoy the other child.

Assertor: You say something to stop this behavior, and if it continues, you ignore it.

Aggressor: You tease the other child about his/her haircut.

Assertor: You tell the teaser that you don't like being teased in a calm, but firm voice.

Aggressor: You broke a toy, but you lie and say the other child did it.

Assertor: You tell the other child how you feel about the situation without getting angry.

Aggressor: You cut into line at the movies in front of the other child.

Assertor: You say that cutting in line is breaking the rules. Then you decide on the best solution to the problem without arguing or fighting.

Managing Conflict

Conflicts are an inevitable part of life, and children's ability to constructively resolve conflicts can be an important part of their social success. The activities in this section are particularly important for children with problems in anger control and aggressiveness. Studies suggest that teaching children positive alternatives to getting angry is the most direct way to reduce school behavior problems.

As with other social skills, the ability to resolve conflicts may be an inherited predisposition. If you watch children on the playground, you will probably observe some children who seem to be natural peacemakers—the ones most likely to suggest compromises to any kind of problem. These children realize that compromise does not mean giving in or giving up; rather, it means suggesting alternative solutions that enable people who disagree to come to an agreement. They understand that compromise consists of a choice that will make everyone happy, even though it may not be exactly what anyone would have chosen originally.

When no adult guidance is present, groups of children tend to view the more outgoing children as leaders, and conflict management skills convey a special power of their own. As children develop these skills, they are more likely to become leaders in their peer group. When shy or overly aggressive children begin to learn conflict management skills, you may observe a natural movement of their status within the group, which will in turn stimulate them to develop other social relationships.

Remember to be patient in teaching these new skills. It has taken time for children to learn their current behaviors, and it will take time for them to learn new behaviors. An effective social skills program will reinforce a child's newly acquired skills in every part of life: the home, the classroom, the playground, and even the cafeteria and school bus.

Learning Objective: To teach children the meaning of conflict

Skill: Conflict resolution

Ask the group, "What is conflict?" Brainstorm ideas and write them on the blackboard or a large sheet of paper.

Tell them:

Conflict begins when two people want the same thing, or when people disagree about the same thing. Conflicts are a part of everyday life—everyone has them. Sometimes they can be resolved easily, and sometimes resolving them takes a lot of thinking and talking.

When you're having a conflict with someone, it's a good idea to ask yourself, "Is it more important for me to get what I want or to keep a good relationship with the other person?" This question is important because arguing with someone may affect your relationship. No one likes to argue, and when people argue, they often end up with hurt feelings. If you are always arguing with people, it will be hard to have good friends.

Lead a discussion on conflicts children have had at home, school, or elsewhere. Ask whether and how the conflicts were resolved. If they haven't been resolved yet, talk about ideas for conflict resolution.

Learning Objective: To teach children that conflicts within themselves can affect their relationships with others

Skill: Conflict resolution, emotional awareness

Ask the group, "What is a 'personal conflict'?" Ask for examples and write them on the blackboard or a large sheet of paper.

Tell them:

> *Every day, you may have personal conflicts within yourself. Other people may not know that you are trying to decide on one choice or another, one thing to say or another, and so on. These inner conflicts are always going on, and sometimes we don't even realize it.*
>
> *When an inner conflict causes a lot of dissatisfaction or pain, it can make you feel really frustrated. You may end up taking your bad feelings out on others. You may not even realize what you're doing, but the other person certainly will. She may become angry with you without understanding why, and in turn, you may be confused about why she's angry.*

Have group members think of times when it was difficult to make a decision. Perhaps both options seemed like the right thing to do, or maybe they wanted to do both and had to decide on one. Ask them how they felt when they finally chose, and whether they were satisfied with their choice.

Then, ask the children to think about other people they know who may have inner conflicts. Give examples like:

- Your mother or father might be thinking about changing jobs.
- Your older brother may be trying to decide what college to go to, or whether to go to college at all.
- Your friend may be thinking of joining a team and worrying about how much time it will take.

Discuss how other people's inner conflicts have affected the members of the group.

Learning Objective: To teach children that both parties are responsible in any conflict between two people

Skill: Conflict resolution

Tell the group:

> There are many different types of conflicts. You can have a conflict within yourself or with someone else. Groups can have conflicts too. Sometimes one group of children doesn't like another group of children. Even countries have conflicts. Sometimes these conflicts are so serious that the countries go to war.
>
> Conflicts between two people are probably the most common kind, and they can happen even when you are having fun. They are inevitable, because there will always be times when both people want different things or see a situation differently. Sometimes, people blame others for conflicts. But you can't have an argument alone, and arguments aren't anyone's fault—they happen because two people disagree. Learning to resolve conflicts peacefully is an important part of getting along with others.

Have the children think of positive actions that can only be done with two or more people—having a catch, hugging, playing checkers, and so on. Then, for each example, have them think of a conflict that could happen. For example, Jon and Matt are having a catch. Jon throws the ball way over Matt's head, and Matt thinks Jon did it on purpose. Ask the children to talk about recent conflicts they have had that were resolved quickly and positively.

Learning Objective: To teach children that some conflicts require an apology

Skill: Social communication, conflict resolution

Ask the group, "What is something you have done that required an apology?" Write answers on the blackboard or a large sheet of paper.

Tell them:

> *Apologizing is often hard to do. When you have a conflict with someone or hurt someone's feelings, it's often not intentional. When you are accused of doing something wrong, you may get defensive, especially if you don't think the accusation is fair. The last thing you'll feel like doing is apologizing. But apologizing—realizing that you did something wrong, saying you're sorry, and really meaning it—shows that you care. There are several things to remember about apologizing:*
>
> - *Try to fully understand what your actions did to hurt the other person.*
> - *Never blame your actions on someone or something else.*
> - *Validate the person's feelings by saying, "If I were you, I'd probably feel the same way."*
> - *Make it clear what you're sorry about.*
> - *Don't expect the situation to be instantly better. It might take awhile.*
> - *After you apologize, let the other person talk.*

Have pairs of children role-play one of the following scenarios. Each child in the pair should have a chance to give and receive an apology.
- You said you would call your friend, but you forgot.
- You borrowed a book from your friend, and then you lost it.
- You were talking to someone else, and when your friend came along, you didn't include her in the conversation.
- You had a bad day and were very sarcastic toward your friend.

Then have a group discussion about why some apologies end conflict and others do not.

Learning Objective: To teach children that some times are better than others for resolving conflicts

Skill: Conflict resolution, social awareness

Ask the group to think about times when it might be very hard to resolve a conflict. Offer examples: when a parent has a headache, or when it's late at night and everyone is tired. Then, ask them to suggest times when it might be easier to resolve a conflict, such as at a family or class meeting.

Tell them:

> *Some conflicts must be resolved right away. For example, if you and your brother or sister want to watch different TV shows, you have to work the problem out then and there. Other conflicts—usually the more serious ones—should be worked out at times when the people involved are prepared to tackle the problem calmly and logically. For example, if a friend of yours was being mean to you, you might want to ask him to come over after school so you can talk about it. When there are serious conflicts between people, it is always best for them to find a good time to work their problems out.*

Distribute Activity Sheet 94. Each child will need a red and a blue crayon. After the activity is done, talk about how to create situations or recognize times that are better for working out a conflict. Some examples are: inviting someone for a walk; waiting until after dinner when the family is relaxed and still at the table; or following a quiet activity, like reading.

Name _____   **Date** _____

Use a blue crayon to color the pictures that show a good time to work out a problem. Use a red crayon to color the pictures that show a bad time to work out a problem.

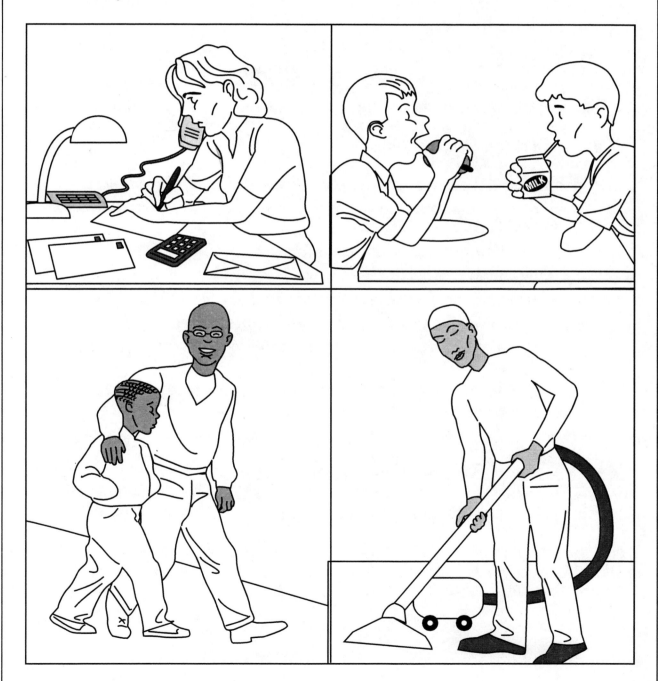

Learning Objective: To teach children that resolving conflict is easier when both people are calm

Skill: Conflict resolution, self-control

Tell the group:

> *Conflicts come from issues that people differ over and the feelings that grow from their disagreement. Expressing your feelings can be difficult when you're trying to resolve a conflict, but it is important to let the other person know how you feel. If you and the other person are calm, you have a much better chance of being able to talk about the conflict and your feelings about it.*
>
> *Here are some steps you can take to deal with conflicts calmly.*
> * *Before starting to talk, take five deep breaths and let them out slowly.*
> * *Relax the muscles of your face and body.*
> * *Describe what you want.*
> * *Tell the other person what's bothering you and how you feel.*
> * *Listen carefully to the other person's wants and feelings.*
> * *Talk about the conflict as a mutual problem—it belongs to both of you.*
> * *If you find yourself getting angry or upset, take deep breaths again and try to relax.*
> * *If feelings are starting to take over the discussion, take a break.*

Ask for the group to pretend they are angry—tensing their muscles, making annoyed faces, assuming an angry posture, etc. Then, ask a volunteer to describe a recent problem he had with someone, using an angry voice.

Next, ask the group to relax, taking five deep breaths and loosening up their bodies. Now, ask a volunteer to use a calm voice to describe a problem he recently had with another person. Discuss the differences in the way people felt, thought, and talked.

Compromising*

Learning Objective: To teach children the benefits of compromising

Skill: Conflict resolution, social awareness

Ask the group to define "compromise," and provide examples.

Tell them:

> *People compromise when they agree to make concessions, or "meet in the middle." Neither person gets exactly what she wants, but each gets some of what she wants.*

> *It's often necessary to compromise when two people have a difference of opinion on how something should be done, or what they each want to do. If you can learn this skill, it will help you get along better with others.*

Distribute Activity Sheet 96. The children should decide how each of the pairs could compromise, and then share their answers.

Name ——————————— Date ———————

How can these children work out a compromise? In each example, write your answer on the lines between the children.

I need that crayon.

That's the color I want to use now.

There's hardly any cereal left in the box.

We both need to eat breakfast.

I want to watch Monster Mountain.

I want to watch the football game.

Learning Objective: To teach children that both people can experience a positive outcome in a conflict

Skill: Conflict resolution

Ask the group, "Can you think of a time you had a problem with someone and you worked it out so that you both felt good?"

Tell them:

Many people think that, in a conflict, one person has to win and another has to lose. But if both people work together, they can come up with a win-win solution that satisfies both of them.

Suppose you and your brother or sister each like a different TV show that's on at the same time. Here are three possible outcomes:

1. The bigger or louder person watches what he or she wants.

2. A parent comes and turns off the TV and no one gets to watch.

3. One person watches the show he or she wants, and then it is the other person's turn to choose the next show. The next day, the person who went second in choosing the show gets to go first.

In the first example, one of you wins and one of you loses. In the second example, you both lose. In the third example, there is a compromise where each person gives a little and gets a little. That's a win-win solution.

Distribute Activity Sheet 97. After it is completed, have the children talk about their win-win solutions.

Win-Win Solutions

Name ——————————————————— Date ———————————

Under each picture, write a possible win-win solution for the situation.

Learning Objective: To teach children to resolve a conflict by negotiating

Skill: Conflict resolution, social communication

Ask the group, "Have you ever gone back and forth with someone about something you want?"

Tell them:

If your parents want you to do your homework right after school, and you want to do it before bedtime, you can come to a compromise by negotiating. Negotiating is a back-and-forth communication that ends in an agreement in which everyone involved gets some of what they want. You may have seen negotiation in your own family, perhaps when you decide what restaurant to go to or what movie to see.

The steps in negotiating include:
1. *State the problem.*
2. *State what you want.*
3. *State why you want it.*
4. *Focus on things you both want.*
5. *Create win-win alternatives.*
6. *Evaluate the alternatives.*
7. *Come up with an agreement and make a plan of action.*

Have two children come up with a conflict, and coach them as they solve it by negotiation, using the above steps. Then divide the group into pairs and have all the children practice negotiating. At the end of this activity, ask for volunteers to talk about their experience.

Learning Objective: To teach children to resolve conflicts with the help of a third party

Skill: Conflict resolution

Tell the group:

> *Peer mediation is a way to resolve conflicts with the help of a peer who is not involved in that conflict. Without taking sides, the peer mediator helps the people who are in conflict come to an agreement. Mediation creates a friendly environment. Each person is listened to and heard, and eventually both are able to respond to the conflict from the other's point of view.*
>
> *Before beginning mediation, the participants agree to:*
>
> 1. *Meet at an agreed-upon time and place.*
> 2. *Respect the mediator's authority to preside over the session.*
> 3. *Share their wants, needs, feelings, and views of the conflict.*
> 4. *Listen to the other person without interrupting.*
> 5. *Avoid labeling, judging, or blaming the other person.*
> 6. *Remain calm and control their anger.*
> 7. *Brainstorm solutions without evaluating them.*
> 8. *Come up with a solution that is agreeable to both.*

Suggest a conflict, and ask two children to role-play participants in peer mediation. Initially, model the role of the mediator yourself. Then, have a volunteer from the group serve as the peer mediator.

Note: Peer mediation is a structured process that takes time and training for children to master. It is normally done as part of a school-wide program. This activity can serve to introduce the group to the idea of peer mediation.

Learning Objective: To teach children to attack problems, not people

Skill: Conflict resolution

Ask the group, "What do you think 'fair fighting' means?" Brainstorm ideas and write them on the blackboard or a large sheet of paper.

Tell them:

> *There are rules that boxers and wrestlers should follow when they fight. These rules are intended to keep them from getting hurt and to keep the match fair. There are rules for fighting with words too. If two children are arguing over something they both want, they can fight fairly so that neither gets hurt.*
>
> *Here are rules that are important to keep in mind when you are arguing with other people:*
>
> - *Don't call them names or make fun of them in any way.*
> - *Stand or sit at least an arm's length away.*
> - *Don't touch them.*
> - *Don't threaten them.*
> - *Don't interrupt them when they are talking.*
> - *When it is your turn to talk, speak as calmly as you can.*
> - *When you have both had a chance to express your opinions, try to work out a compromise.*

Ask the children to think about recent conflicts they have had with family members or friends. Have them talk about whether the fight was fair, or if not, what fair-fighting rules were broken. If children report that they are often in situations that involve fighting, hand out copies of Activity Sheet 100.

I agree to the rules of Fair Fighting. I:
- Won't call other people names or make fun of them in any way.
- Will stand or sit at least an arm's length away.
- Won't touch other people during a fight.
- Won't threaten other people.
- Won't interrupt other people when they are talking.
- Will speak as calmly as I can, when it is my turn to talk.
- Will try to work out a compromise after we have all expressed our opinions.

Signed: _____

Date: _____

FAIR FIGHTING

Learning Objective: To teach children what can happen if conflicts remain unresolved

Skill: Social awareness

Tell the children:

It's important to solve conflicts for many reasons. If a conflict remains unresolved, negative feelings remain. Here's what can happen:
- *Everyone is "for himself" and sticks to his position.*
- *No one gets what he wants or needs.*
- *Emotions flare and tempers get out of hand.*
- *Feelings are hurt and relationships suffer.*
- *Violence may result.*

If people work together toward conflict resolution, positive feelings and outcomes emerge:
- *People listen to each other, respect one another, and cooperate.*
- *Views are clarified and problems are dealt with.*
- *Relationships and communication are improved.*
- *Better ideas are produced to solve the conflict.*
- *Everyone gets what he wants and needs.*

Distribute Activity Sheet 101. When the children have completed it, ask them to share their positive and negative outcomes for each situation.

Name ———————————————————— Date ————————————

Think of a positive and negative outcome for each situation.

A girl accidentally drops paint on a boy's pants.

Positive outcome _____

Negative outcome _____

A boy borrows another boy's bat and loses it.

Positive outcome _____

Negative outcome _____

A girl makes plans with one friend and tells the other she's busy.

Positive outcome _____

Negative outcome _____

A girl says she'll clean her room but doesn't.

Positive outcome _____

Negative outcome _____

SKILLS INDEX